Laboratory Activities Manual
Teacher Edition

blue.msscience.com

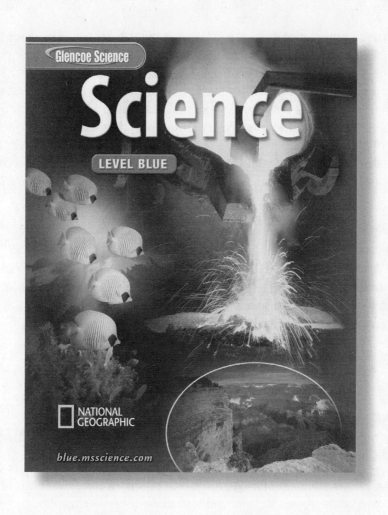

Glencoe Science

Science
LEVEL BLUE

NATIONAL GEOGRAPHIC

blue.msscience.com

McGraw Hill Glencoe

New York, New York   Columbus, Ohio   Chicago, Illinois   Peoria, Illinois   Woodland Hills, California

To the Teacher

Activities in *Glencoe Science Laboratory Activities Manual* do not require elaborate supplies or extensive pre-lab preparations. They are designed to explore science through a stimulating yet simple and relaxed approach to each topic. Helpful comments, suggestions, and answers to all questions are provided at the back of the *Teacher Edition.*

Activities in this laboratory manual are student-oriented. The scientific conclusions desired are not valid for any student unless he or she is directly involved in obtaining them. The activities should be performed by students only with your supervision. Directions are straightforward, so students can follow them easily. Students should be able to work through a problem to a satisfactory answer. The design of the manual is such that students should be interested enough to do their own investigating and not accept conclusions made by someone else. Students should discover their own mistakes through a review of the introductory statement, **Strategy,** and **Procedure.** If students still cannot reach a satisfactory conclusion, assistance in interpreting data may be needed.

Each activity can be torn from the book and handed in when the lab has been completed. Although the labs are not designed as a grading device, they can serve as a measure of progress for you and your students.

Most labs can be completed in a single class period. Some do not require the entire period; others require portions of two or more consecutive periods. Some require a preliminary setup followed by several inspections.

Glencoe

The *McGraw·Hill* Companies

Send all inquiries to:
Glencoe/McGraw-Hill
8787 Orion Place
Columbus, OH 43240-4027

ISBN 0-07-867164-7

Printed in the United States of America.

5 6 7 8 9 10 113 09

Table of Contents

Inquiry in the Science Laboratory

What is inquiry?

The process of inquiry models actual science practice, encourages problem-solving strategies, and develops critical-thinking skills. Students are actively involved in the learning process when they determine materials, procedures, and the topics and questions they want to investigate.

Inquiry can range from a very structured activity for those students who need more guidance, to a more open-ended approach in which students design their investigations. We encourage you to modify the labs in this manual in a manner that best supports your students.

Why is inquiry important?

Inquiry activities, such as those in *Glencoe's Laboratory Activities Manual*, will help students develop educational, career, and life skills. Students learn how to think for themselves, how to solve problems, and how to apply prior knowledge to new situations.

How can this book help?

Glencoe's Laboratory Activities Manual is structured to give support to both teachers and students. Important scientific concepts are the core of each lab. Students gain practice in developing and testing their own hypotheses, designing experiments, gathering and analyzing data, and communicating their conclusions to their peers. Teachers are given strategies to guide students who need additional structure and to encourage students who are ready for more open-ended exploration.

Suggestions for Incorporating Inquiry in the Science Classroom

Inquiry in science does take extra time, just as it would in a research lab. Here are some ways you might be able to efficiently incorporate inquiry into your classroom.

- Supply various materials that are related to the concept you are trying to convey and allow students to explore them in groups for about 15 minutes. Have groups brainstorm ideas and list questions they have about those concepts. Have them list materials they will need. As a class or on your own, eliminate those questions that cannot be answered in the classroom. Gather any additional materials that are needed and allow students to begin their explorations the next day or the next week.

- Have students brainstorm questions they would like to explore. As a class, choose 1 or 2 reasonable questions that each group will explore in its own way. (This is very helpful if you are trying to cover a specific topic.)

- Give your students a more guided activity that relates hard-to-understand concepts and skills. Then, allow them to explore on their own with a wider variety of materials. Make sure you allow time for debriefing so the students (and you) will understand what they learned from the experience.

Suggestions for Incorporating Inquiry in the Science Classroom   continued

- Students will need practice doing inquiry before they should be allowed to explore completely on their own. Be sure to give them lots of practice in using the tools of science so that their explorations are more successful.

- Encourage students to rely on their data and not on what they think the answer should be. If their data are unexpected, help them to problem-solve what might have happened.

Developing Process Skills

Basic Process Skills

Observe: Students use one or more senses to learn more about objects and events.

Classify: Students group objects or events based on common properties and/or categorize based on existing relationships among objects or events.

Infer: Students propose interpretations, explanations, and causes from observed events and collected data.

Communicate: Students convey information verbally, both in oral and written forms, and visually through graphs, charts, pictures, and diagrams.

Measure in SI: Students identify length, area, volume, mass, and temperature to describe and quantify objects or events.

Predict: Students propose possible results or outcomes of future events based on observations and inferences drawn from previous events.

Calculate: Students transfer or apply ordering, counting, adding, subtracting, multiplying, and dividing to quantify data where appropriate.

Complex Process Skills

Interpret Data: Students explain the meaning of information gathered in scientific situations.

Form Hypotheses: Students make an informed assumption in order to draw out and test its logical consequences.

Experiment: Students test hypotheses or predictions under conditions in which variables are both controlled and manipulated.

Formulate Models: Students construct mental, verbal, or physical representations of ideas, objects, or events. The models are then used to clarify explanations or to demonstrate relationships.

Analyze Results: Students evaluate the outcome of an experiment to determine if it is reasonable. They should be able to draw conclusions and make inferences from the results.

Introducing/Reviewing Laboratory Work

Following proper techniques when using laboratory equipment helps prevent accidents and cuts down on the cost of replacement materials and devices. Students' success also is increased as their familiarity with the devices and their measurement and analysis skills increase. To facilitate student success in the classroom laboratory, first familiarize yourself with the general organization of Glencoe's science activities. The organization varies according to the type of activity. Then orient the students to the laboratory setting. This includes reviewing equipment and correct handling procedures with them, the use of SI units in their activities, and assessing their readiness for work in the laboratory.

Organization of Glencoe Science Laboratory Activities

- An **introductory statement** explains the science concepts involved in the activity. Specific information for the investigation of the problem is re-emphasized. This statement appears under the investigation title.

- A **strategy** or **list of objectives** provide objectives for student performance. If the student does not understand the goal(s) of the activity, a rereading of the section is advised.

- **Materials** is the list of all materials or possible materials needed for the activity. The **Materials** section should be previewed so that any supplies to be contributed by students may be obtained in advance. Be sure to assemble these materials *before* the beginning of a class period.

- A **safety precautions** section provides **icons** to prompt safety awareness and general **warning statement(s)** pertinent to the activity.

- Some labs include a section that states the **problem** or **what will be investigated**.

- Some labs have students state a **hypothesis**.

- **Procedure** is the step-by-step set of instructions for the activity. You may want to discuss the procedure with students before they begin the activity. Pre-activity discussions help prevent misuse of equipment and injuries that can result from careless use of the glassware, burners, and/or corrosive chemicals. Specific **safety warning statements** are placed appropriately in the **Procedure** section.

- **Data and Observations** includes sample graphs, charts, and tables to help improve students' analysis skills. Emphasis should be placed on the need to record all observations during and at the completion of the activity. In many cases, recorded data provide the necessary link in cause-and-effect relationships. Each student should do his or her own computations except in those activities where group work or class averages are required.

- An **analysis** or **questions and conclusions** section contains discussion questions and blanks for student answers at the end of each activity. These questions are designed to review main ideas, to direct attention to key parts of the procedure, and to relate the material to science concepts and applications. Answering these questions promotes and reinforces student learning.

- A **strategy check** or **hypothesis check** section allows students to evaluate the activity. If a student can place a checkmark in the blank provided, he or she has gained a skill, interpreted a concept, or learned a process.

Evaluating Activity Work

Evaluation of the activities and of the general outcomes of laboratory work is a difficult task. Pure recognition and recall tests are not usually suitable for evaluating laboratory experience. Evaluation methods that depend on accurate observation, recognition of pertinent data, and ability to reason logically are more suitable for measuring outcomes of laboratory work. This type of evaluation may be done through periodic checking of student notebooks or individual or group conferences. You may also require students to submit laboratory reports. Laboratory reports should include
- a clearly stated problem.
- a procedure outlined in detail.
- data organized in good form and understandable; may include
  a. labeled diagrams.
  b. labeled and titled graphs.
  c. data tables.
- conclusions that answer the problem based on data obtained in the activity.
- a report that is clear enough to serve as a future review of the material.

The following questions should be answered in evaluating an activity report.
- Is the report written clearly enough so that an uninformed person could read it and know exactly what was being attempted, how it was done, and what conclusions were reached?
- Can the student duplicate the experiment using the report alone as a guide?

Achievement tests designed to assess understanding of course content are an important evaluation technique for laboratory work. Knowledge should be obtained through correct laboratory methods.
- You may wish to observe techniques used, correctness of procedures, and results obtained. An observational checklist based on objectives could be used.
- You may wish to direct students to perform a laboratory task in a practical test. Students should be able to satisfactorily complete this test before beginning laboratory work. For this test, set up equipment stations in the classroom. At each station, provide instructions.

Station 1: Lighting a Laboratory Burner
Equipment: laboratory burner, rubber hose, gas outlet, gas lighter or safety matches
Instructions: Correctly set up and light the burner and adjust the flame.

Station 2: Decanting and Filtering
Equipment: two beakers—one containing a mixture of water and sand; stirring rod; filter paper; funnel; ring stand
Instructions: Decant the clear liquid from the residue. Correctly set up the equipment for a filtration procedure.

Station 3: Using the Balance
Equipment: balance, rubber stopper
Instructions: Correctly carry the balance from Station 3 to your desk and back to Station 3. Determine the mass of the rubber stopper.

Evaluating Activity Work   continued

Station 4: **Measuring Temperature**
  Equipment: thermometer, beaker of water
  Instructions: Position the thermometer correctly and determine the temperature of the water in the beaker.

Station 5: **Measuring Volume**
  Equipment: graduated cylinder containing colored water
  Instructions: Determine the volume of water in the graduated cylinder.

Station 6: **Identifying Parts of a Microscope**
  Equipment: microscope, labels
  Instructions: Correctly identify the labeled parts of this microscope.

Station 7: **Using a Microscope**
  Equipment: microscope, prepared slide
  Instructions: Correctly carry the microscope from Station 7 to your desk and back to Station 7. Place the slide on the stage and bring the slide into sharp focus.

Station 8: **Inserting Glass Tubing into a Rubber Stopper**
  Equipment: glass tubing, glycerol or soapy water, one-hole rubber stopper, cloth towel
  Instructions: Insert the glass tubing into the rubber stopper.

Introducing/Reviewing Laboratory Safety Guidelines

Safe Laboratory Conduct

Whether you are a first-time or very experienced teacher, a review of safety guidelines is in order. This section deals with behaviors and actions that foster a safe learning environment. Because you serve as the role model for the behavior in the laboratory that you expect from your students, first review the safety guidelines for teachers. Then, on the first day of classes, introduce or review the safety guidelines that are the students' responsibility.

Teacher Safety Guidelines

- Thoroughly review your local safety regulations and this manual. Modify any activities to comply with your local regulations. For example, open flames are NOT permitted in some states or communities.

- Be trained in first aid and CPR.

- Be aware of students with allergies or other medical conditions that might limit their activities or require special protective equipment, such as facemasks.

- Have a list of substances to be used in lab activities made available to the doctor of any pregnant teacher or student so that limitations may be determined beforehand.

- NEVER leave students unattended in the classroom or field setting.

- NEVER be alone or out of earshot of someone when you prepare lab activities or equipment.

- Always wash your hands with antibacterial soap and warm water upon entering the laboratory, after live cultures have been handled, after cleanup, and before removing safety goggles.

- NEVER perform an investigation on any animal that might be a health hazard to humans or cause pain or suffering to the animal.

- Use protista and other invertebrates for lab or field activities involving animals when possible. Protista represent a wide variety of organisms and can be obtained in large quantities.

- A qualified adult supervisor who has had training in the proper care and handling of laboratory animals must assume responsibility for the conditions of any activity that involves living vertebrates. NO activity/investigation should be conducted that involves drugs, organisms pathogenic to humans or other vertebrates, ionizing radiation, surgical procedures, or carcinogens unless the procedures have been approved by and will be performed or supervised by a qualified biomedical scientist.

Teacher Safety Guidelines continued

- Have students notify you beforehand if they plan to bring in a pet for observation.

- Instruct students about the hazards involved with wild animals and your school's policy and local and state laws regarding their capture and use in the classroom/laboratory. **WARNING:** *Wild animals may exhibit unpredictable behaviors, may become dangerous as they mature, and if declawed, may not be accepted by zoos and will probably die if released into the wild.* **WARNING:** *There is the potential of contracting rabies from any infected warm-blooded animal.*

- It is recomended that you purchase fumigated, steam sterilized materials. **WARNING:**

  - *Owl pellets can be a source of salmonella.*

  - *Bird nests contain many organisms that can cause diseases.*

  - *Bird eggs, even if disinfected when first acquired, will decay after a few days from gases building up in them. Rotten eggs produce noxious odors.*

  - *Some insects carry diseases that are serious if transmitted to humans.*

Presenting Safety Guidelines to Students

- Review the use and location of safety equipment, evacuation guidelines, and first aid procedures. Refer to fire drill regulations and a chart of emergency procedures, which should be posted in a prominent place in the laboratory. Assign safety partners and explain their role in helping during emergencies.

- Discuss safe disposal of materials and laboratory cleanup policy.

- Preview Glencoe's science activities with students and discuss the safety icons and their meanings (see p. 17). Point out the warning statements and the importance of heeding them. Distribute the Safety Symbols reference sheet (see p. 14).

- Distribute and discuss Student Laboratory and Safety Guidelines (see p. 15). Emphasize proper attitudes for working in the laboratory and field and review or present school rules regarding the consequences of misbehavior. Stress the need for safe practices on the part of everyone involved. Then distribute the Student Science Laboratory Safety Contract found on p. 16. You may wish to have each student and parent or guardian sign a safety contract at the beginning of each course. Review the safety guidelines and safety contract with students at least once a month.

Preparation of Solutions

It is important to use safe laboratory techniques when handling all chemicals. Many substances may appear harmless but are, in fact, toxic, corrosive, and very reactive. Always check with the supplier. Chemicals should never be ingested. Be sure to use proper techniques to smell solutions or other agents. Always wear safety goggles and an apron. Observe the following precautions.

1. Always add acids to water, never the reverse.
2. When sodium hydroxide is added to water, a large amount of thermal energy is released. Use extra care when handling this substance.
3. Poisonous/corrosive liquid and/or vapor. Use in fume hood if possible.
   Example: hydrochloric acid
4. Poisonous and corrosive to eyes, lungs, and skin.
   Examples: acids, silver nitrate, iodine, potassium permanganate
5. Poisonous if swallowed, inhaled, or absorbed through the skin.
   Example: silver compounds

Aluminum nitrate solution ($Al(NO_3)_3$), 0.1 M: For a 0.1 M solution, dissolve 3.75 g of aluminum nitrate nonahydrate in 100 ml water.

Baking soda (sodium bicarbonate) solution: To prepare a 0.25% solution, dissolve 0.5 g baking soda (sodium hydrogen carbonate) in 200 mL of water.

Cobalt nitrate solution ($Co(NO_3)_2$), 1 M: For a 1 M solution, dissolve 29.1 g of cobalt nitrate hexahydrate in 100 ml water.

Copper (II) nitrate solution ($Cu(NO_3)_2$), 0.1 M: For a 0.1 M solution, dissolve 1.87 g of copper nitrate hydrate in 100 ml water.

Copper (II) sulfate solution ($CuSO_4$), 0.1 M: For a 0.1 M solution, dissolve 2.49 g of copper (II) sulfate pentahydrate in 100 ml water.

Glucose solution, 0.1 M: For a 0.1 M solution, dissolve 1.8 g of glucose in 100 ml water.

Iron (II) nitrate solution ($Fe(NO_3)_2$), 0.1 M: For a 0.1 M solution, dissolve 4.04 g of iron nitrate nonahydrate in 100 ml water

Magnesium nitrate solution ($Mg(NO_3)_2$), 0.1 M: For a 0.1 M solution, dissolve 2.56 g of magnesium nitrate hexahydrate in 100 ml water.

Nickel nitrate solution ($Ni(NO_3)_2$), 0.1 M: For a 0.1 M solution, dissolve 2.90 g of nickel nitrate hexahydrate in 100 ml water.

Sodium chloride ($NaCl$), 0.1 M: For a 0.1 M solution, dissolve 0.58 g of sodium chloride (table salt) in 100 ml water.

Sodium hydroxide ($NaOH$), 0.1 M: For a 0.1 M solution, carefully add 0.40 g of sodium hydroxide to 50 ml water and mix to dissolve. Add water to make 100 ml.

Sodium hypochlorite solution ($NaClO$), 2.5%: Dilute 50 ml household bleach (5% NaClO) with 50 ml water (note: bleach concentrations can vary from 3–6%—check bottle label)

Sucrose solution, 0.1 M: For a 0.1 M solution, dissolve 3.4 g of sucrose in 100 ml water.

Sulfuric acid solution (H_2SO_4), 0.1 M: For a 0.1 M solution, carefully add 0.98 g of concentrated sulfuric acid to 50 ml water and mix. Add water to make 100 ml.

Zinc nitrate solution ($Zn(NO_3)_2$), 0.1 M: For a 0.1 M solution, dissolve 2.79 g of zinc nitrate hexahydrate in 100 ml water.

Lab Preparation

Laboratory Equipment and Supplies

This table of equipment and inexpensive, easily accessible materials can help you prepare for your science class.

It is assumed that goggles, laboratory aprons, gloves, tap water, textbooks, paper, calculators, pencils, and pens are available for all activities.

Non-Consumables	
Item	**Experiments used in**
1.5-V batteries (2)	23-1
9-V battery and battery clip	16-1
alligator clips (4)	16-1, 23-1, 23-2
aluminum foil	23-1
bag of mixed beans, small	2-1
bag, small paper	4-2
baking pan	8-1
balance	19-2
basketball	11-2
beaker	17-1
beaker, 400-mL	17-2
beaker, 500-mL	3-2
beaker, ovenproof, 250-mL	1-2
beakers, 250-mL (3)	21-1, 23-2
beans, brown (101)	4-2
beans, white (17)	4-2
block diagram, Figure 1	9-1
books (or boxes)	12-2
bowl, large ceramic or stainless steel	8-1
bowling ball	18-2
boxes with lids, clear plastic (2)	5-2
burner	17-1
cardboard sheet, 10 cm $\times$ 10 cm	16-1
cardboard, stiff	12-1
chart in Figure 1	15-2
clock with second hand or timer	5-2, 17-2
closet (or locker)	14-1
colored pencils	4-2, 5-1, 5-2, 7-1, 9-1, 10-1, 10-2, 12-1, 21-2
compass	24-1
container, large plastic	2-1
containers, medium plastic (2)	2-1

Non-Consumables (continued)

Item	Experiments used in
containers, plastic, 500-mL (2)	21-2
containers, small plastic (4)	2-1
copy of the periodic table	15-1
coverslips (2)	6-2
cup, paper (or plastic or film canister)	24-2
cups, clear plastic (2)	5-2
diode	23-1
disk magnet, no more than 5 mm in diameter (can also be cut out of a flexible magnetic strip)	24-2
disk magnets (4)	24-2
dowel, wood, about 50 cm long	20-1
droppers (3)	1-1, 6-2, 8-1, 14-1
electric fan, small	12-2
eraser, rubber	23-1
eye hook	19-1
flashlight	11-2, 13-1
globe, mounted on axis	11-1
graduated cylinder	1-2, 5-2
graduated cylinder, 100-mL	21-2, 23-2
graduated cylinder, 25-mL	1-1
graphite (pencil lead)	23-1
hair dryer	21-1
heat lamp, mounted	12-1
hot plate	1-2, 7-2, 17-2, 21-1
ice chest	21-1
LED (light-emitting diode)	16-1
lightbulb holders (2)	23-1
lightbulbs (2)	23-1
magnifying lens	16-2
marker	8-2
marking pen	5-2
mass, 1kg	20-1
measuring cup	8-2
measuring spoons	3-2
meterstick	8-1, 8-2, 10-1, 10-2, 11-1, 13-1, 18-1, 19-2, 20-1, 20-2
metric ruler	3-2
microplate, 24-well	16-1, 17-2
microplate, 96-well	16-2
microscope	6-2

Non-Consumables (continued)

Item	Experiments used in
microscope slides (2)	6-2
multi-gear bicycle	20-2
nail	3-1
nail, medium sized	13-1
Nutrition Facts labels from various packaged foods	3-1
paper clip	23-1
pen cap, plastic	23-1
pencil	4-1, 15-1, 24-2
permanent marker	6-1, 21-1
pillow, large	18-2
pipe, copper	23-1
pipette, plastic microtip	16-2, 17-2
pipettes, plastic (7)	16-1, 17-2
pot, medium-to-large mouthed	7-2
resistor, 1,000-W	16-1
rod, glass	23-1, 23-2
roller skates	18-1
rubber bands	13-1
rubber bands or strings, 8 cm (2 pieces)	3-2
ruler	12-2, 24-2
scissors	7-2, 8-2, 9-1, 11-2, 13-1, 13-2, 20-1, 21-2, 24-2
screw, brass	23-1
set of masses	19-1
skating safety equipment (helmet, pads)	18-1
shovel, small (or scoop)	9-2
soil	12-1
spoon	17-1
spring balance	18-1
spring scale	20-1
spring scale calibrated in newtons	19-1
steel wool	17-1
stick, wooden	23-1
stopwatches (5-10)	11-1, 18-1, 18-2, 19-2, 20-1
storage box and lid, clear plastic	12-1
string	11-1, 20-1
sunlight or bright lamp	5-2
table, large	19-2
tape measure, flexible	21-1

Non-Consumables (continued)

Item	Experiments used in
test tube	3-2, 17-1
test-tube rack	1-1, 1-2, 3-2
test tubes, 18-mm × 150-mm (4)	1-1, 1-2
test-tube holders (4)	1-2, 17-1
textbook	8-1, 8-2, 11-2
thermometer (2)	4-1, 5-2, 12-1, 17-2
thermometer, Celsius, alcohol	21-2
timer	21-2
tongs	7-2, 17-1
toy car with free spinning wheels, small	19-2
voltmeter	23-2
washers, iron or lead (3 or 4)	17-2
watch (or clock)	12-1, 17-1
wire strippers	23-1
wire, copper, insulated, 20 cm lengths (4)	16-1, 23-1
wires (2)	23-2
wood block, 30 cm long	20-2
wood block, about 5 cm × 10 cm × 26 cm	19-1

Consumables

Item	Experiments used in
2% milk	3-1
adding machine tape, 4-4.5 m	10-2
aluminum foil	17-1
aluminum foil, heavy gauge	23-2
aluminum nitrate solution, 0.1 M Al(NO$_3$)$_3$	16-2
aluminum strip	23-2
ammonia	1-1
antacid tablets, fizzing (6)	5-2
apple sauce	3-1
baking soda	17-1
baking soda solution	1-1
balloon, rubber	14-1
balloons (9)	8-2, 21-1
bouillon soup	1-2
box open only at one end, small	6-1
candy-coated chocolates, 4 red and 3 green	14-2
candy-coated peanuts, 4 red and 3 green	14-2
canned green beans	3-1
canned peaches	3-1

Consumables (continued)

Item	Experiments used in
cardboard, small piece	11-2
cardboard, thick, approximately 50 cm × 50 cm	8-2
cardboard, thin	9-1
chocolate pudding	3-1
clay	9-2
$Co(NO_3)_2$ solution, 1 M	17-2
coffee can, empty	8-2
common nail, Fe	7-1
construction paper, black	13-1, 21-2
construction paper, red, green or blue (the color should make water drops easy to see)	12-2
construction paper, white	21-2
container, at least 25 cm × 20 cm × 15 cm (or approximately shoe-box size)	9-2
copper (II) sulfate solution, $CuSO_4$, 0.1 M	17-1
copper nitrate solution, 0.1 M $Cu(NO_3)_2$	16-2
copper strip	23-2
corn flakes	3-1
corn syrup, dark	3-2
correction fluid, white (or chalk or markers)	13-1
cotton balls	1-2
dialysis bagging cut into two 6-8 cm strips	3-2
food coloring (3 drops)	21-1
food coloring, red, blue, and green	8-2
frozen dinner	3-1
glucose solution, 0.1 M glucose	16-1
glue or paste	9-1
graph paper	10-1, 12-1, 15-1, 24-1
green pepper, with seeds, cut in half	2-2
hamburger buns	3-1
hydrochloric acid, 0.1 M	23-2
ice, crushed	12-2, 21-1
iron nitrate solution, 0.1M $Fe(NO_3)_2$	16-2
Italian or other salad dressing	3-1
labels	1-1, 1-2
litmus paper, red or blue	1-2
magnesium nitrate solution, 0.1 M $Mg(NO_3)_2$	16-2
maple syrup	3-1
margarine	3-1
margarine tubs, plastic, 1 lb. (2)	8-2

Consumables (continued)

Item	Experiments used in
matches	17-1
mayonnaise	3-1
metal strips (eight 1mm × 10mm strips of each: aluminum, Al; copper, Cu; iron, Fe; magnesium, Mg; nickel, Ni; and zinc, Zn)	16-2
modeling clay, about 300 g	19-2
newspaper	8-2, 9-2, 12-2
nickel nitrate solution, 0.1 M Ni(NO$_3$)$_2$	16-2
objects to use in making trace fossils (3)	9-2
orange juice	3-1
paint stirrers, wooden (3)	8-2
paintbrushes, old (3)	8-2, 16-2
paper	4-1, 24-2
paper towels	8-1, 16-1, 16-2, 17-1, 23-2
pitcher of tap water	8-1
plaster of paris	8-2
plastic foam wrap for padding packages, not made from corn or organic materials (several sheets)	7-2
potassium permanganate (2 or 3 large crystals)	3-2
potato chips	3-1
pots, small plastic, filled with soil and planted with grass seed (4)	6-1
red cabbage juice, 40-mL	1-1
sand, not dirt	12-2
soda pop	3-1
sodium chloride (rock, crystalline)	16-1
sodium chloride solution, 0.1 M NaCl	16-1
sodium hydroxide solution, 0.1 M NaOH	16-1
sodium hypochlorite solution (NaClO), 1 M 2.5%	17-2
sponge	8-2
steel wool	17-1
string (or thread)	17-2, 19-2
sucrose solution, 0.1 M sucrose	16-1
sugar cubes (sucrose)	16-1
sulfuric acid solution, 0.1 M H$_2$SO$_4$	16-1
tape	13-1, 16-1, 18-1, 19-2, 21-2
tape, adhesive	11-1
tape, clear	9-1
tape, masking	5-2, 20-1, 24-2
tape, masking, 4 cm (2 pieces)	3-2

Consumables (continued)

Item	Experiments used in
tubes of toothpaste in different colors (white, green striped)	8-2
tuna fish	3-1
vanilla extract, 2-mL	14-1
vanilla wafers or other cookies	3-1
varieties of "soil"—sand, potting soil, pea gravel, mulch, shredded dried leaves, fresh grass cuttings (3)	9-2
vegetable or tomato juice	3-1
vinegar	1-1, 23-2
water	1-2, 3-2, 5-2, 6-1, 7-2, 8-2, 21-1, 21-2, 23-2
water collected from the surface of a pond	6-2
water collected near the bottom of a pond	6-2
water, distilled	16-1, 16-2
waxed paper	12-2
whole wheat bread	3-1
wire tie, plastic coated	20-1
wood splint	17-1
zinc nitrate. 0.1 M $Zn(NO_3)_2$	16-2

Answers to Student Laboratory Equipment Worksheets

Figure 1

1. Graduated cylinders 2. Florence flask 3. Beakers 4. Crucible 5. Petri dish
6. Evaporating dish 7. Erlenmeyer flask 8. Long-stem funnel 9. Watch glass

Figure 2

1. Test tubes 2. Test-tube rack 3. Square-bottomed test tubes 4. Rubber stoppers
5. Corks 6. Test-tube holder 7. Test-tube brush

Figure 3

1. Utility clamp 2. Wire gauze 3. Metal ring 4. Laboratory burner 5. Gas inlet
6. Ring stand

Figure 4

1. Stirring rod 2. Funnel

Figure 5

1. Thermometer 2. Pipette 3. Rubber tubing 4. Pinch clamp 5. Dropper 6. Spatula
7. Stirring rod 8. Triangular file 9. Forceps 10. Scalpel

Figure 6

1. Eyepiece 2. Revolving nosepiece 3. High-power objective lens 4. Low-power
objective lens 5. Stage 6. Diaphragm 7. Adjustment knob 8. Light

Figure 7

1. Hickman still head 2. Conical reaction vials 3. Air reflux condenser 4. Claisen head
5. Hirsch funnel 6. Filter flask 7. Erlenmeyer flask (10 mL) 8. Funnel 9. Reaction tubes
10. Magnetic stir bars 11. Connector with support rod 12. Pipette 13. Stopper
14. Spatula 15. Centrifuge tube 16. Glass tube connectors 17. Syringe 18. Flasks
19. Tubing 20. One-way stopcock 21. Connectors 22. Thermometer connectors

Figure 8

1. Berol pipettes 2. Blue litmus vial and litmus discs 3. Microstand 4. Plastic tubing
(long and short) 5. Zinc electrode 6. Zinc coil 7. Iron electrode 8. Various tubes
9. Microspatulas 10. Dual well comboplate 11. Microburner 12. Syringe
13. Chromatography paper strips 14. pH color chart 15. Gas collecting vial
16. Microcaps 17. Compass 18. Microlids 19. Current LED indicator

Table of Contents

Getting Started

Science is the body of information including all the hypotheses and experiments that tell us about our environment. All people involved in scientific work use similar methods for gaining information. One important scientific skill is the ability to obtain data directly from the environment. Observations must be based on what actually happens in the environment. Equally important is the ability to organize these data into a form from which valid conclusions can be drawn. These conclusions must be such that other scientists can achieve the same results in the laboratory.

To make the most of your laboratory experience, you need to continually work to increase your laboratory skills. These skills include the ability to recognize and use equipment properly and to measure and use SI units accurately. Safety also must be an ongoing concern. To help you get started in discovering many fascinating things about the world around you, the next few pages provide you with:

- a visual overview of basic **laboratory equipment** for you to label
- a reference sheet of **SI units**
- a reference sheet of **safety symbols**
- a list of your **safety responsibilities** in the laboratory
- a **safety contract**

Each lab activity in this manual includes the following sections:

- an investigation **title** and introductory section providing information about the problem under study
- a **strategy** section identifying the **objective(s)** of the activity
- a list of needed **materials**
- safety concerns identified with **safety icons** and **caution statements**
- a set of step-by-step **procedures**
- a section to help you record your **data and observations**
- a section to help you **analyze your data** and record your **conclusions**
- a closing **strategy check** so that you can review your achievement of the objectives of the activity

Laboratory Equipment

Figure 1

1. _____   2. _____

3. _____

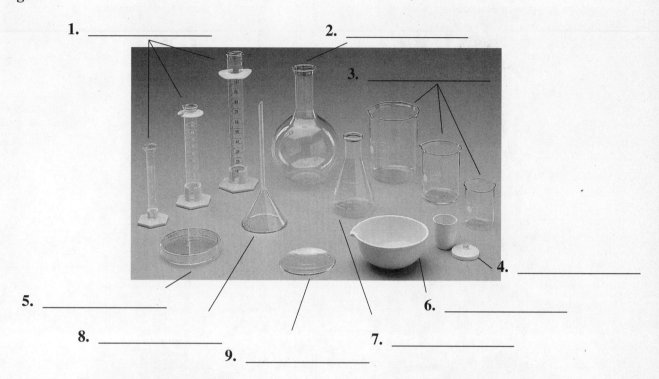

4. _____

5. _____   6. _____

8. _____   7. _____

9. _____

Figure 2

1. _____

3. _____   2. _____

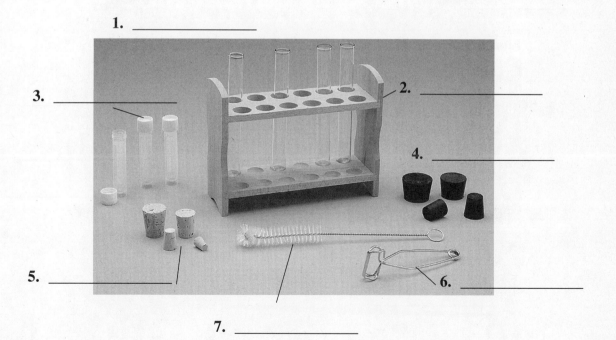

4. _____

5. _____   6. _____

7. _____

Laboratory Equipment (continued)

Figure 3

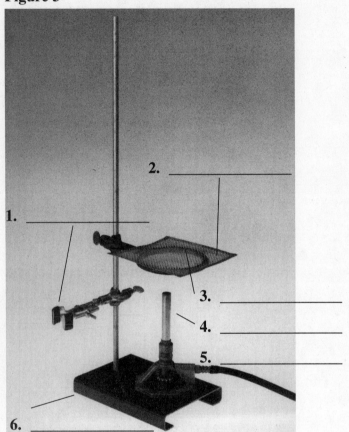

1. _____
2. _____
3. _____
4. _____
5. _____
6. _____

Figure 4

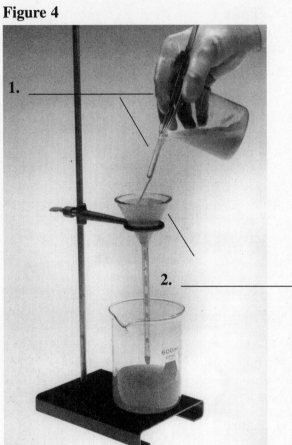

1. _____
2. _____

Figure 5

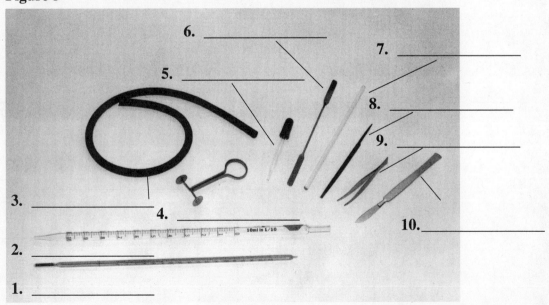

1. _____
2. _____
3. _____
4. _____
5. _____
6. _____
7. _____
8. _____
9. _____
10. _____

Laboratory Equipment (continued)

Figure 6

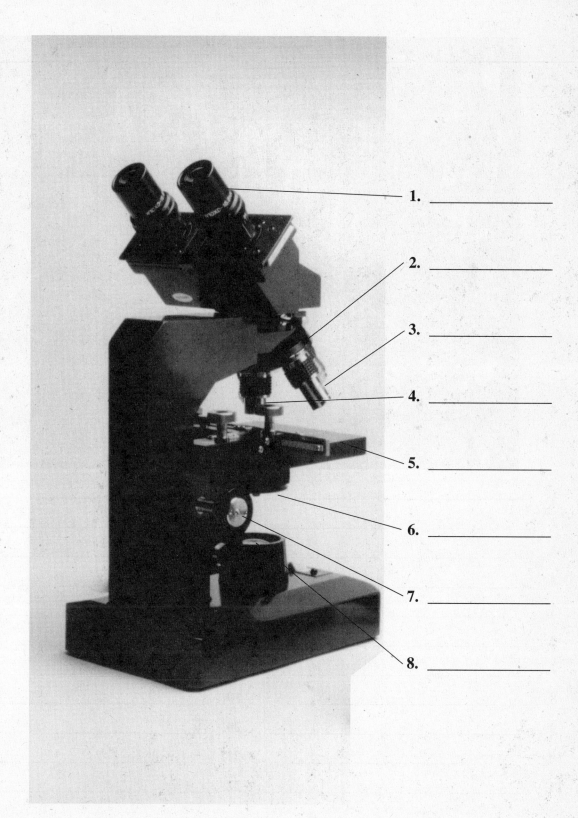

1. _____

2. _____

3. _____

4. _____

5. _____

6. _____

7. _____

8. _____

Laboratory Equipment (continued)

Figure 7

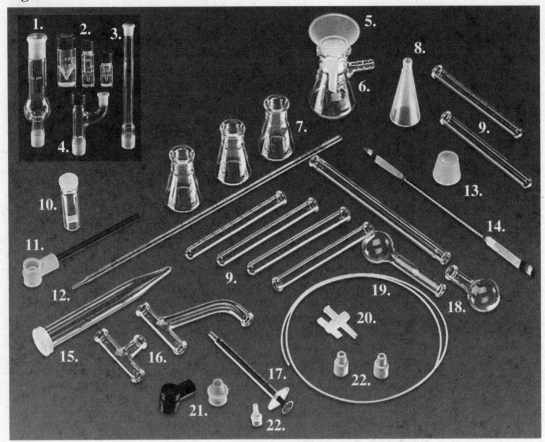

1. _____

2. _____

3. _____

4. _____

5. _____

6. _____

7. _____

8. _____

9. _____

10. _____

11. _____

12. _____

13. _____

14. _____

15. _____

16. _____

17. _____

18. _____

19. _____

20. _____

21. _____

22. _____

Laboratory Equipment (continued)

Figure 8

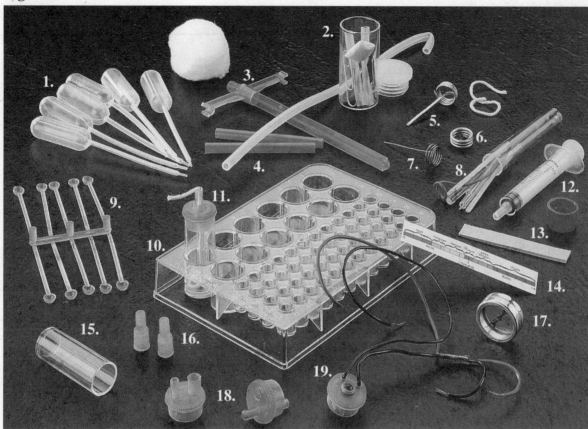

1. _____   11. _____
2. _____   12. _____
3. _____   13. _____
4. _____   14. _____
5. _____   15. _____
6. _____   16. _____
7. _____   17. _____
8. _____   18. _____
9. _____   19. _____
10. _____

SI Reference Sheet

The International System of Units (SI) is accepted as the standard for measurement throughout most of the world. Frequently used SI units are listed in **Table 1** and some supplementary SI units in **Table 2.**

Table 1

	Frequently Used SI Units
Length	1 millimeter (mm) = 100 micrometers (μm) 1 centimeter (cm) = 10 millimeters (mm) 1 meter (m) = 100 centimeters (cm) 1 kilometer (km) = 1,000 meters (m) 1 light-year = 9,460,000,000,000 kilometers (km)
Area	1 square meter (m^2) = 10,000 square centimeters (cm^2) 1 square kilometer (km^2) = 1,000,000 square meters (m^2)
Volume	1 milliliter (mL) = 1 cubic centimeter (cm^3) 1 liter (L) = 1,000 milliliters (mL)
Mass	1 gram (g) = 1,000 milligrams (mg) 1 kilogram (kg) = 1,000 grams (g) 1 metric ton = 1,000 kilograms (kg)
Time	1 s = 1 second

Table 2

Supplementary SI Units			
Measurement	**Unit**	**Symbol**	**Expressed in base units**
Energy	joule	J	$kg \cdot m^2/s^2$
Force	newton	N	$kg \cdot m/s^2$
Power	watt	W	$kg \cdot m^2/s^3$ or J/s
Pressure	pascal	Pa	$kg/m \cdot s^2$ or $N \cdot m$

Sometimes quantities are measured using different SI units. In order to use them together in an equation, you must convert all of the quantities into the same unit. To convert, you multiply by a conversion factor. A conversion factor is a ratio that is equal to one. Make a conversion factor by building a ratio of equivalent units. Place the new units in the numerator and the old units in the denominator. For example, to convert 1.255 L to mL, multiply 1.255 L by the appropriate ratio as follows:

$$1.255 \text{ L} \times 1,000 \text{ mL}/1 \text{ L} = 1,255 \text{ mL}$$

The unit L cancels just as if it were a number.

Temperature measurements in SI often are made in degrees Celsius. Celsius temperature is a supplementary unit derived from the base unit kelvin. The Celsius scale (°C) has 100 equal graduations between the freezing temperature (0°C) and the boiling temperature of water (100°C). The following relationship exists between the Celsius and kelvin temperature scales:

$$K = °C + 273$$

SI Reference Sheet (continued)

To convert from °F to °C, you can:

1. For exact amounts, use the equation at the bottom of **Table 3**, or
2. For approximate amounts, find °F on the thermometer at the left of **Figure 1** and determine °C on the thermometer at the right.

Table 3

Figure 1

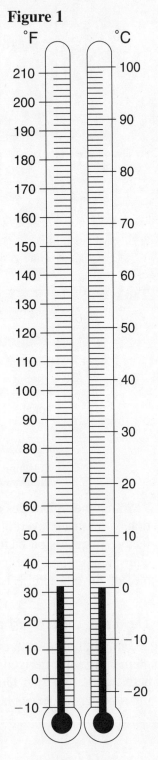

SI Metric to English Conversions			
	When you have:	**Multiply by:**	**To find:**
Length	inches	2.54	centimeters
	centimeters	0.39	inches
	feet	0.30	meters
	meters	3.28	feet
	yards	0.91	meters
	meters	1.09	yards
	miles	1.61	kilometers
	kilometers	0.62	miles
Mass and weight*	ounces	28.35	grams
	grams	0.04	ounces
	pounds	0.45	kilograms
	kilograms	2.20	pounds
	tons	0.91	metric tons
	metric tons	1.10	tons
	pounds	4.45	newtons
	newtons	0.23	pounds
Volume	cubic inches	16.39	cubic centimeters
	milliliters	0.06	cubic inches
	cubic feet	0.03	cubic meters
	cubic meters	35.31	cubic feet
	liters	1.06	quarts
	liters	0.26	gallons
	gallons	3.78	liters
Area	square inches	6.45	square centimeters
	square centimeters	0.16	square inches
	square feet	0.09	square meters
	square meters	10.76	square feet
	square miles	2.59	square kilometers
	square kilometers	0.39	square miles
	hectares	2.47	acres
	acres	0.40	hectares
Temperature	Fahrenheit	$\frac{5}{9}(°F - 32)$	Celsius
	Celsius	$\frac{9}{5}°C + 32$	Fahrenheit

* Weight as measured in standard Earth gravity

SAFETY SYMBOLS

(handwritten note overlapping page:)
Convert
Standard→Metric

Microscope
parts &
lab equipt

Scientific
method
Lab

HAZARD	EXAMPLES	PRECAUTION	REMEDY
Special disposal proce-... ...ed to be fol-...	certain chemicals, living organisms	Do not dispose of these materials in the sink or trash can.	Dispose of wastes as directed by your teacher.
...s or other ...materials ...t be harmful ...s	bacteria, fungi, blood, unpreserved tissues, plant materials	Avoid skin contact with these materials. Wear mask or gloves.	Notify your teacher if you suspect contact with material. Wash hands thoroughly.
...hat can burn ...eing too cold	boiling liquids, hot plates, dry ice, liquid nitrogen	Use proper protection when handling.	Go to your teacher for first aid.
...ls or glass-... ...can easily ...or slice skin	razor blades, pins, scalpels, pointed tools, dissecting probes, broken glass	Practice common-sense behavior and follow guidelines for use of the tool.	Go to your teacher for first aid.
...anger to res-...act from	ammonia, acetone, nail polish remover, heated sulfur, moth balls	Make sure there is good ventilation. Never smell fumes directly. Wear a mask.	Leave foul area and notify your teacher immediately.
...anger from ...shock or	improper grounding, liquid spills, short circuits, exposed wires	Double-check setup with teacher. Check condition of wires and apparatus.	Do not attempt to fix electrical problems. Notify your teacher immediately.
...s that can ...skin or ...embranes of ...atory tract	pollen, moth balls, steel wool, fiberglass, potassium permanganate	Wear dust mask and gloves. Practice extra care when handling these materials.	Go to your teacher for first aid.
...can react ...estroy tissue ...materials	bleaches such as hydrogen peroxide; acids such as sulfuric acid, hydrochloric acid; bases such as ammonia, sodium hydroxide	Wear goggles, gloves, and an apron.	Immediately flush the affected area with water and notify your teacher.
...may be poi-...ouched, ...swallowed.	mercury, many metal compounds, iodine, poinsettia plant parts	Follow your teacher's instructions.	Always wash hands thoroughly after use. Go to your teacher for first aid.
...e chemicals ...ited by ...e, spark, or ...eat.	alcohol, kerosene, potassium permanganate	Avoid open flames and heat when using flammable chemicals.	Notify your teacher immediately. Use fire safety equipment if applicable.
...e in use, ...fire.	hair, clothing, paper, synthetic materials	Tie back hair and loose clothing. Follow teacher's instruction on lighting and extinguishing flames.	Notify your teacher immediately. Use fire safety equipment if applicable.

...lothing ...rotection
...his symbol appears ...hen substances ...uld stain or burn ...othing.

Animal Safety
This symbol appears when safety of animals and students must be ensured.

Handwashing
After the lab, wash hands with soap and water before removing goggles.

Student Laboratory and Safety Guidelines

Regarding Emergencies

- Inform the teacher immediately of *any* mishap—fire, injury, glassware breakage, chemical spills, and so forth.
- Follow your teacher's instructions and your school's procedures in dealing with emergencies.

Regarding Your Person

- Do NOT wear clothing that is loose enough to catch on anything and avoid sandals or open-toed shoes.
- Wear protective safety gloves, goggles, and aprons as instructed.
- Always wear safety goggles (not glasses) when using hazardous chemicals.
- Wear goggles throughout entire activity, cleanup, and handwashing.
- Keep your hands away from your face while working in the laboratory.
- Remove synthetic fingernails before working in the lab (these are highly flammable).
- Do NOT use hair spray, mousse, or other flammable hair products just before or during laboratory work where an open flame is used (they can ignite easily).
- Tie back long hair and loose clothing to keep them away from flames and equipment.
- Remove loose jewelry—chains or bracelets—while doing lab work.
- NEVER eat or drink while in the lab or store food in lab equipment or the lab refrigerator.
- Do NOT inhale vapors or taste, touch, or smell any chemical or substance unless instructed to do so by your teacher.

Regarding Your Work

- Read all instructions before you begin a laboratory or field activity. Ask questions if you do not understand any part of the activity.
- Work ONLY on activities assigned by your teacher.
- Do NOT substitute other chemicals/substances for those listed in your activity.
- Do NOT begin any activity until directed to do so by your teacher.
- Do NOT handle any equipment without specific permission.
- Remain in your own work area unless given permission by your teacher to leave it.
- Do NOT point heated containers—test tubes, flasks, and so forth—at yourself or anyone else.
- Do NOT take any materials or chemicals out of the classroom.
- Stay out of storage areas unless you are instructed to be there and are supervised by your teacher.
- NEVER work alone in the laboratory.
- When using dissection equipment, always cut away from yourself and others. Cut downward, never stabbing at the object.
- Handle living organisms or preserved specimens only when authorized by your teacher.
- Always wear heavy gloves when handling animals. If you are bitten or stung, notify your teacher immediately.

Regarding Cleanup

- Keep work and lab areas clean, limiting the amount of easily ignitable materials.
- Turn off all burners and other equipment before leaving the lab.
- Carefully dispose of waste materials as instructed by your teacher.
- Wash your hands thoroughly with soap and warm water after each activity.

Student Science Laboratory Safety Contract

I agree to:

- Act responsibly at all times in the laboratory.

- Follow all instructions given, orally or in writing, by my teacher.

- Perform only those activities assigned and approved by my teacher.

- Protect my eyes, face, hands, and body by wearing proper clothing and using protective equipment provided by my school.

- Carry out good housekeeping practices as instructed by my teacher.

- Know the location of safety and first aid equipment in the laboratory.

- Notify my teacher immediately of an emergency.

- NEVER work alone in the laboratory.

- NEVER eat or drink in the laboratory unless instructed to do so by my teacher.

- Handle living organisms or preserved specimens only when authorized by my teacher, and then, with respect.

- NEVER enter or work in a supply area unless instructed to do so and supervised by my teacher.

[This portion of the contract is to be kept by the student.]

[Return this portion to your teacher.]

I, _____, [print name] have read each of the statements in the Student Science Laboratory Safety Contract and understand these safety rules. I agree to abide by the safety regulations and any additional written or verbal instructions provided by the school district or my teacher. I further agree to follow all other written and verbal instructions given in class.

_____   _____

Student Signature   Date

I acknowledge that my child/ward has signed this contract in good faith.

_____   _____

Parent/Guardian Signature   Date

A Scientific Method

Chapter 1

When scientists are asked questions, they might not know the answers. They think of the possible answers, called hypotheses, and experiment to find the correct answers. Using the results of the experiment, they might need to form another hypothesis and test it. This way of solving a problem is called a scientific method.

Strategy

You will predict whether or not red cabbage juice will remain red when chemicals are added to it.
You will test your prediction with an experiment.
You will observe what happens and record your observations.
You will draw conclusions based on your observations.

Materials

graduated cylinder (25 mL)   ammonia
40 mL red cabbage juice   baking soda solution
test tube rack   labels
4 test tubes (18 × 150-mm)   3 droppers
vinegar (Keep containers closed
when not in use.)

WARNING: *Do not mix ammonia with vinegar. May react vigorously.*
WARNING: *Ammonia fumes are poisonous. Avoid inhaling the vapors.*
WARNING: *Do not taste, eat, or drink any materials used in this lab.*
WARNING: *Inform your teacher if you come in contact with any chemicals.*

Procedure

1. In the space below, predict what will happen to the red cabbage juice when vinegar, ammonia, and baking soda solution are added to it.

   _____

   _____

2. Label four test tubes, 1, 2, 3, and 4.
3. Add 10 mL of red cabbage juice to each test tube.

WARNING: *Avoid contacting any chemicals with clothes or skin. Rinse with water if spilled.*

4. Add 10 drops of vinegar to test tube 1.
5. Add 10 drops of ammonia to test tube 2.
6. Add 10 drops of baking soda solution to test tube 3.
7. Do not add anything to test tube 4. This is the control. The control is the part of the experiment that is not tested.
8. Record your observations in the Table.

Data and Observations

Test tube	Substance added	Color
1		
2		
3		
4		

Laboratory Activity 1 (continued)

Questions and Conclusions

1. **a.** Was your prediction correct?

   _____

   b. What part of the scientific method is predicting?

   _____

2. Do all chemicals have the same effect on red cabbage juice?

   _____

3. Why did you record the color changes?

   _____

   _____

   _____

4. What steps in the scientific method did you use?

   _____

   _____

5. What is the purpose of the control in an experiment?

   _____

   _____

6. Why is a hypothesis called an educated guess?

   _____

   _____

7. Was your experimenting a way of proving your hypothesis?

   _____

   _____

8. How did your hypothesis change after experimenting?

   _____

   _____

Strategy Check

_____ Can you make a prediction?

_____ Can you test your prediction and record what happened?

_____ Can you draw conclusions based on your observations?

Using a Scientific Method

If scientists hypothesized that there are organisms in the air, how could they test their hypothesis? Do you believe that there are organisms in the air? What makes you think so? You can experiment to test your hypotheses.

Strategy

You will use a scientific method to determine if organisms are found in the air.
You will use tubes containing various foods that may or may not allow for the growth of organisms.
You will observe and test for the presence of organisms.

Materials

4 test tubes (18 × 150-mm)
test-tube rack
graduated cylinder
bouillon soup

water
beaker (oven proof, 250-mL)
hot plate
4 test-tube holder

cotton balls
labels
litmus paper (red or blue)

Procedure

1. Pour 15 mL of bouillon soup into two test tubes.
2. Add 15 mL of water to two other test tubes.
3. Place each test tube into a test-tube holder and then place all the holders into a small beaker half filled with water. Place the beaker on a hot plate. Allow the tubes to remain in the water for at least 15 min. while boiling.
4. Remove all tubes from the hot water bath. **WARNING:** *Do not touch the tubes. They are hot.*
5. Place the test tubes in a test-tube rack. Seal one bouillon tube and one water tube securely with a cotton plug. Leave the remaining two tubes open.
6. Label each tube with your name, date, and either "water" or "soup".
7. Examine all the tubes after one week. Compare the appearance of the two tubes containing soup. Are they cloudy or clear? Hold them towards the light to help decide. Record your observations using the words *cloudy* or *clear* under the column marked Appearance in Table 1. Compare the appearance of the two water tubes. Again use *cloudy* or *clear* under Appearance in the table.

8. Test each test tube to determine if the liquids are acid, base, or neutral. Remove the cotton plugs and dip a small piece of litmus paper into each tube. Use a new piece of litmus paper for each tube. HINT: Blue litmus turns red in an acid and red litmus turns blue in a base. No change in either paper means that the liquid is neutral. Use the words *acid, base,* or *neutral* to complete the column marked *litmus paper test* in the table.
9. Carefully smell each tube. See Figure 1. Record in the column marked *Odor* in the table whether the tubes smell meaty, spoiled, or have no smell (none).
10. Give all test tubes to your teacher for proper disposal.

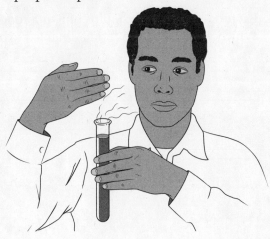

Laboratory Activity 2 (continued)
Data and Observations
Table 1

Tube	Appearance	Litmus paper test	Odor
1. soup, open			
2. soup, sealed			
3. water, open			
4. water, sealed			

Questions and Conclusions

1. Bacteria growing in a liquid will cause the liquid to become cloudy. Which tube(s) had bacteria growing in them? Which tube(s) remained clear?

_____

_____

_____

2. Bacteria growing in a liquid cause the liquid to change to an acid. Comparing the litmus paper test between the opened and sealed soup tubes, which tube(s) became acid? Which tube (s) remained neutral?

_____

_____

_____

3. Bacteria growing in a liquid often results in a spoiled odor. Which tube(s) had a spoiled odor?

_____

_____

4. Bacteria will grow in liquids only if a food supply is present. Which tube(s) contained food? Which tube(s) had no food available for bacteria (water is not a food)?

_____

_____

_____

Laboratory Activity 2 (continued)

5. What evidence do you have that bacteria came into the tubes only from the air?

_____

_____

_____

6. What evidence do you have that bacteria need food in order to live, grow, and increase in number?

_____

_____

7. Why were all the tubes first boiled in hot water? **HINT**: Boiling destroys bacteria.

_____

_____

8. What conclusion can you make if the sealed soup tube became cloudy and had a foul odor?

_____

_____

_____

9. What evidence do you have that you breathe organisms as part of the air?

_____

_____

_____

_____

10. Predict what experimental results might be expected if both tubes of soup and water were boiled and sealed. Explain.

_____

_____

11. Predict what experimental results might be expected if both tubes of soup were boiled but were left open.

_____

_____

12. Predict what experimental results might be expected if both tubes were not boiled and were not sealed.

_____

Strategy Check

_____ Did you use a scientific method to test the hypotheses that there are organisms in the air?

_____ Can you determine which tubes do or do not have organisms growing in them?

Identifying Bean Traits

You have learned that every living thing has certain inherited traits. It is often easy to recognize the physical traits of animals—cats with striped coats or solid coats; dogs with floppy ears or short ears. But plants also have traits that are recognizable. How can you classify plants according to their traits?

Strategy

You will identify the physical traits of beans.
You will classify a bag of mixed beans into two main groups and four sub-groups based on the presence or absence of physical traits.

Materials

small bag of mixed beans
large plastic container
medium plastic containers(2)
small plastic containers(4)

Procedure

1. Empty your bag of beans into the large plastic container.
2. Examine your beans closely. Make a list of the physical traits of your beans. Traits define color, shape, and other distinctive features of the beans.

3. Of the traits you observe, choose one trait that allows you to divide your beans into two groups—Group 1 and Group 2.
4. Divide the beans into Groups 1 and 2 according to the trait you chose in step 3. Use the two medium containers to hold the beans in Groups 1 and 2.
5. Examine Groups 1 and 2 closely. Choose a trait that will allow you to divide Group 1 into two sub-groups—Groups 1a and 1b. Then choose a trait that allows you to divide Group 2 into two sub-groups—Groups 2a and 2b.
6. Divide the beans according to the traits you chose in step 5. Use the four small containers to hold the beans in the four sub-groups.

Data and Observations

In the diagram below, fill in the traits you used to classify your beans.

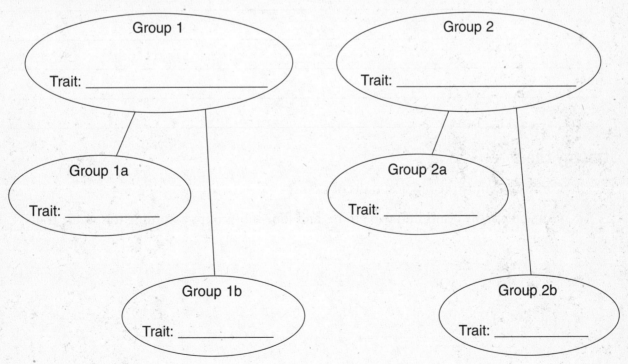

Laboratory Activity 1 (continued)

Questions and Conclusions

1. What trait did you use to divide the entire bag of beans into two groups? Explain your reasons for choosing this trait over another.

_____

_____

_____

_____

_____

2. What traits did you choose to divide the two groups of beans into four sub-groups? Was making the four sub-groups easier or more difficult than making the first two groups of beans? Why?

_____

_____

_____

_____

_____

3. How many different kinds of beans were there in your original bag of beans? Why do you think there are so many different kinds of beans?

_____

_____

_____

_____

_____

Strategy Check

_____ Can you identify the physical traits of beans?

_____ Can you classify beans into two groups and four sub-groups according to specific traits?

How many plants can a pepper produce?

You have learned that environmental factors influence how many organisms survive in an area. These factors can be either living or nonliving. Most organisms overproduce, meaning that, for example, if one plant produced 1,000 seeds and each seed grew into a new plant the next year, 1,000 new plants would result. If each of these 1,000 new plants produced 1,000 seeds, then a total of 1,000,000 plants would result. Environmental factors help prevent such large numbers from growing.

Strategy

You will count the number of seeds in one green pepper.

You will calculate the average number of green pepper seeds in the class.

You will determine how many plants would grow from these green pepper seeds over a five year period.

Safety Precautions

Materials

green pepper (with seeds), cut in half

Procedure

1. Remove the seeds from the pepper and count them. Record the number in Table 1 in the Data and Observations section.

2. Collect seed totals from the rest of the class to calculate the average number of seeds in a green pepper. Add the seed totals, then divide by the number of people in the class. Round the average off to the nearest hundred. Record the numbers in Table 1.

3. Complete the data table using the following assumptions:
   a. One green pepper plant grew in the first year.

   b. The first green pepper plant produced the rounded-off average number of seeds.

   c. All seeds produced by the green pepper plant grow into new plants.

   d. Every new plant always produces the rounded-off number of seeds each year.

4. Determine how many new green pepper plants will grow in the second year. Record this number in Table 2.

5. Determine how many new green pepper plants will grow in the third, fourth, and fifth years. Record these numbers in Table 2.

Data and Observations

Table 1

Seeds in green pepper	
Seeds in all green peppers	
Number of students in a class	
Average number of green pepper seeds	
Class average rounded to nearest 100	

Laboratory Activity 2 (continued)

Table 2

Year	Number of pepper plants
1	
2	
3	
4	
5	

Questions and Conclusions

1. How many green pepper plants were recorded for the first year? How many plants will be produced in the fifth year?

_____

2. Name some of the living and nonliving factors in the environment that would prevent every green pepper seed from growing into a new plant.

_____

_____

_____

_____

3. What are the chances that 100,000,000 green pepper plants will eventually result from the seeds of one green pepper plant? Explain your answer.

_____

_____

_____

_____

4. How is it adaptive for organisms to overproduce?

_____

_____

_____

_____

Laboratory Activity 2 (continued)

5. What other factors have you learned about that help ensure the survival of a species?

_____

_____

_____

_____

Strategy Check

_____ Can you determine the number of seeds in one green pepper?

_____ Can you calculate the average number of seeds per pepper for your class?

_____ Can you determine how many plants will grow from one green pepper each year for five years?

Minerals and Good Health

LAB 1 Laboratory Activity

Chapter 3

Minerals and other inorganic substances are essential for a healthy growing body. Calcium, phosphorus, and magnesium all contribute to bone growth. Iron helps your blood carry oxygen from your lungs and bring back carbon dioxide. Minerals bond with organic molecules to help your cells function properly. Minerals are especially important for young people. Children who grow up in some of the poorer regions of the world are at highest risk for mineral deficiencies. Most of the minerals people need come from various foods and from water. What you eat has a huge impact on what minerals you get. Scientists have come up with a standard recommendation for quantities of each mineral required to maintain a healthy body. The standard, called Recommended Daily Allowance (RDA), provides guidelines as to how much of each mineral the human body can use each day. The Reference Daily Intake, based on the RDA, provides a guideline as to how much of each mineral a person should consume each day in order to maintain healthy mineral levels. Labels on foods are required to include information about how much of the RDA for various vitamins and minerals that product provides per serving. In this laboratory activity, you will be looking at RDAs, RDIs, and labels for various foods and collecting data on how you can meet your mineral needs.

Strategy

You will research and record the quantities of certain nutritional minerals in typical servings of various foods.

You will determine if these foods satisfy established daily requirements for those minerals.

You will identify which body parts or functions use certain minerals.

Materials

Nutrition Facts labels from various packaged foods
potato chips
frozen dinner
corn flakes
2% milk
whole wheat bread
hamburger buns
margarine
orange juice
tuna fish
mayonnaise
vegetable or tomato juice
canned peaches
vanilla wafers or other cookies
apple sauce
canned green beans
Italian or other salad dressing
chocolate pudding
soda pop
maple syrup

Procedure

1. Choosing from the items for which you have labels in your classroom and the additional items in Table 2, assemble a one day menu for yourself. Enter your selection in Table 1.

2. For each menu item, record the mineral content information in Table 1. You will find this information in the Nutrition Facts panel from the food packaging or in Table 2.

3. Calculate the total mineral intake for each mineral for the day's menu and record your findings in Table 1.

4. Compare your results with the RDIs listed for each mineral in Table 3.

5. Examine Table 1 in your textbook to find other types of foods that might be used to make up any shortcomings in your menu's mineral content. Remember, though, that replacing one food with another to increase a particular mineral might cause a reduction in a different mineral. Record your ideas in the Data and Observations section.

Laboratory Activity 1 (continued)

Data and Observations

Table 1

Menu				
	Sodium (mg)	**Calcium (mg)**	**Potassium (mg)**	**Iron (mg)**
Breakfast				
Lunch				
Dinner				
Total mineral intake				

Laboratory Activity 1 (continued)

Table 2

Type of Food	Mineral–Amount per Serving			
	Sodium (mg)	Calcium (mg)	Potassium (mg)	Iron (mg)
Hamburger	660	20	190	2
Chicken (roast)	70	9	270	8
Beef (roast)	55	10	300	2
Pork chop	70	9	300	9
Pizza (cheese/tomato)	340	240	180	1
Cheddar cheese	610	800	120	4
Cheese (processed)	1360	700	80	5
Egg (scrambled)	1050	60	130	2
Pancake	50	120	140	9
Strawberries (4)	0.5	7	80	0.2
Apple	2	3	90	2
Banana	1	7	350	4
Orange	2	30	150	3
Carrot (raw)	100	50	220	0.6
Broccoli (boiled)	6	80	220	1
Potato (baked)	6	8	550	0.6
Tomato (raw)	3	10	290	0.4
Doughnut	60	70	110	2
Cheesecake	260	70	120	7

Table 3

Mineral	US-RDI
Calcium	1,000 mg
Iron	10 mg, males; 18 mg, females
Potassium	99 mg
Sodium	30–2,300 mg

*Note: RDA for potassium can safely go as high as 2,000 mg

Laboratory Activity 1 (continued)

1. Is there too much or too little of any mineral in your menu, as compared with the RDIs? If so, what do you think is the reason?

   _____

   _____

   _____

2. What foods could you change or add to your menu to increase the minerals your menu is lacking?

   _____

   _____

3. Study the Tables on page 15.
   a. Which type of food in Table 2 is the highest in calcium?

   _____

   b. Does one serving of this food meet the daily requirement for calcium? Explain.

   _____

   _____

Questions and Conclusions

1. Did your menu meet all the RDIs for the four minerals you examined? If not, which minerals fell short?

   _____

   _____

2. Suggest any possible shortcomings you see for the possible replacement foods you listed increase certain minerals in your menu.

   _____

   _____

   _____

3. Did any of the foods you selected provide the entire day's RDI? Which?

   _____

   _____

4. According to Table 1 from your text, what body parts or functions benefit from the minerals you examined?

   _____

   _____

   _____

Laboratory Activity 1 (continued)

5. Do you think it's important for young people to eat a wide variety of foods to get the minerals they need? Why?

_____

_____

_____

Strategy Check

_____ Can you research and record quantities of certain nutritional minerals in typical servings of various foods?

_____ Can you determine if those foods satisfy established daily requirements for those minerals?

_____ Can you identify which body parts or functions use certain minerals?

Transporting Nutrients

LAB 2 Laboratory Activity

Chapter 3

The cells in your body get the nutrition they need by passing substances across their membranes. Some substances pass easily across the membranes. Others need some help in the form of energy or membrane proteins. Membranes that allow some substances to pass through easily, but not others, are called semipermeable membranes. In this laboratory, you will examine some of the processes by which nutrients and wastes enter and leave a cell. Diffusion and osmosis are the most common ways substances pass through a membrane. You will simulate these processes and be able to observe a semipermeable membrane.

Strategy

You will observe diffusion.
You will observe and describe how a semipermeable membrane works.

Materials

water
test tube
potassium permanganate
    (two or three large crystals)
test-tube rack
metric ruler
500-mL beaker
dialysis bagging cut into 2 6–8-cm strips
rubber bands or string (2 pieces, 8 cm)
masking tape (2 pieces, 4 cm)
measuring spoons
dark corn syrup

Procedure

Part A—Observing Diffusion

1. Pour water into a test tube until it is about three-fourths full.
2. Your teacher will put two to three large crystals of potassium permanganate into your test tube. As the potassium permanganate becomes diluted, it will turn a deep purple. **WARNING:** *Potassium permanganate is an irritant, and it will also stain your clothing. Be careful when handling it.*
3. Put the test tube in the test-tube rack. Do not touch or shake the test tube in any way. Note the time in Table 1 in the Data and Observations section.

4. After 10 minutes, observe the color change in the water. Measure the highest point the deep purple color has reached. Record your measurement in Table 1 in the Data and Observations section.
5. Repeat step 4 two more times.

Part B—Observing a Semipermeable Membrane

1. Pour water into a 500-mL beaker until it is about half-full of water. Be sure there is plenty of room to put your bagging in it without spilling the water.
2. Take one end of the dialysis bagging and tie it off securely with a rubber band or string.
3. Open the other end of the bagging. The bagging will probably be very difficult to pry open, just like some supermarket plastic bags. If the tubing is dry, place masking tape on your thumb and forefinger and pull aside the edges of the open end. If it is wet, rub the edges of the open end until they come apart.
4. Place about 1 teaspoon of the dark corn syrup in the bag and tie off that end as you did the other.
5. Place the entire bag, with corn syrup in it, into the water beaker. Record your observations of the bag in Table 2 in the Data and Observations section.
6. Wait for 20 minutes and observe the bag of corn syrup. Record your observations in Table 2 in the Data and Observations section.

Laboratory Activity 2 (continued)

Data and Observations

Table 1

Beginning Time	Height (cm) after 10 Minutes	Height (cm) after 20 Minutes	Height (cm) after 30 Minutes

Table 2

Beginning Observations:
After 20 Minutes:

Questions and Conclusions

1. What happened to the color of the water in the test tube with the potassium permanganate?

_____

_____

_____

Laboratory Activity 2 (continued)

2. What can you conclude about how some cells in your body get some of their nutrition?

_____

_____

_____

3. In the experiment with the corn syrup, did the water enter the bag?

_____

_____

_____

4. Did the corn syrup appear to leave the bag?

_____

_____

_____

5. Which substance do you think has larger molecules—water or corn syrup? Why?

_____

_____

_____

6. This type of barrier is called a semipermeable membrane. What does it mean when the membrane of a human cell is called semipermeable?

_____

_____

_____

Strategy Check

_____ Can you observe diffusion?

_____ Can you observe and describe how a semipermeable membrane works?

LAB 1 Laboratory Activity

Communities

Chapter 4

The human population of an area is made up of all the people who live there. The community in which people live includes other populations as well, populations that might include squirrels, honey bees, and maple trees. All the populations living together in a certain area make up a community. The producers in a community make the energy-rich molecules that can be used as food. The consumers obtain food by eating other organisms, either living or dead, that contain the energy-rich molecules. All the organisms in a community interact with each other.

Strategy

You will study a community.

You will identify organisms in the community that are producers or consumers.

Materials

thermometer
paper
pencil

Procedure

Part A

1. In Table 1 in the Data and Observations section, list four living things commonly found in each type of community shown below. For example, a farm community might have humans, cows, horses, chickens, wheat, corn, and soybeans.

2. Classify the living things listed in Table 1 as producers or consumers. Producers can make their own food and are usually green. Consumers cannot make their own food and usually are not green. Circle the producers and underline the consumers.

Laboratory Activity 1 (continued)

Part B

1. With your teacher's help, choose a nearby community to study.
2. Record in Table 2 the common names of the consumers and producers that you observed in your selected community. Note the approximate number of each type of organism. Continue your list on a separate sheet of paper, if needed.

3. Moisture, light, season of the year, and temperature can influence communities. Observe these conditions in the community you are studying. Then record your observations below in the Data and Observations section.

Data and Observations

Table 1

Type of community	Names of organisms
Farm	
Forest	
Desert	
Ocean	

Table 2

Producers		Consumers	
Type	Number	Type	Number
Example: Grass		Example: Mice	

1. Location: _____

2. Date of observation: _____

3. Amount of direct sunlight: _____

4. Evidence of moisture: _____

5. Air temperature: _____

Laboratory Activity 1 (continued)

Questions and Conclusions

1. Define community.

_____

2. What is a producer?

_____

3. What is a consumer?

_____

4. Do all communities have both consumers and producers? Explain.

_____

_____

5. How many kinds of producers did you find in the community you studied?

_____

_____

6. How many kinds of consumers did you find?

_____

_____

7. Did you find more producers than consumers? Explain why there would be more of one than the other.

_____

_____

8. What do producers provide consumers?

_____

_____

Strategy Check

_____ Can you study a community?

_____ Can you identify the producers and consumers in the community?

Changes in Predator and Prey Populations

Chapter 4

A predator is an animal that kills and eats another animal. A fox is an example of a predator. The prey is the animal killed by a predator. A rabbit is an example of an animal that is prey for the fox.

The sizes of the predator and prey populations can change with time. Biologists sometimes need to know the sizes of certain predator and prey populations. They can sample the population by trapping and/or counting the animals. The result of the samplings changes as the populations change.

Strategy

You will set up a model of predator and prey populations and observe changes in the results you get from sampling as the populations change.

You will construct a graph showing your results.

Materials

101 brown beans
17 white beans
small paper bag
colored pencils

Procedure

Part A—Sampling a Population

1. Read this report about animals on the abandoned Linworth farm.

   The Linworth farm was abandoned in 1990, when an interstate highway was built through it. In April 1997, two biologists decided to study how the fox and rabbit populations on the 40 hectares of farmland were changing. The scientists counted rabbits by trapping and releasing them and counted foxes with binoculars. The biologists trapped and released 23 rabbits; they saw 2 foxes. The scientist continued their observations in the spring and fall for several years.

2. Put 92 brown beans and 8 white beans into a bag. The brown beans represent rabbits, and the white beans represent foxes. Note that these numbers are four times the observed number of animals in the example above. The observed animals are the sample. The larger numbers represent the numbers of rabbits and foxes in the actual populations.

3. Shake the bag with the beans. Select a bean without looking. Record your results in Table 1 in the Data and Observations section. If you picked a brown bean, put a mark under "observed" in the rabbit column. If you picked a white bean, put a mark in the fox column.

4. Return the bean to the bag. Select another bean, record the result in Table 1 and return the bean to the bag. Repeat this procedure until you have results recorded for 25 beans, which is 25 percent of the actual numbers in the populations.

5. Add together the numbers of brown beans selected. Record the number in Table 1. Repeat for the white beans.

Part B—Recording Changes in Populations

1. Examine Table 2, which explains how to change numbers of beans to show how the rabbit and fox populations changed as a result of changes in environmental factors.

Laboratory Activity 2 (continued)

2. Use the information in Table 2 and the method described in Part A to sample the populations of rabbits and foxes nine more times. Enter your data in Table 3.

   a. Start with the information for the first date in Table 2, October 1997. Add and remove beans as directed to represent the changes described.

   b. Select 25 more beans, returning them to the bag each time. Make marks in the appropriate columns in Table 3, and fill in the total number of brown beans and white beans selected.

c. Repeat this procedure for every date in Table 3. When you come to a date in Table 3 that is not included in Table 2, assume there was no change in the populations. However, conduct a new sampling even though the total populations were unchanged.

3. Fill in the graph on the next page using the data from the population samplings that you recorded in Table 3. Use two different colored columns for each date, one for rabbits and one for foxes.

Data and Observations

Table 1

Sampling Data				
Date	**Rabbits (brown beans)**		**Foxes (white beans)**	
	Observed	**Total**	**Observed**	**Total**
April 1997				

Table 2

Changes in Population		
Sampling date	**Rabbit population**	**Fox population**
October 1997	The winter was harsh, and food was inadequate. Many rabbits died. Remove 10 brown beans.	Foxes ate pheasants as well as rabbits. Fox numbers increased. Add 2 white beans.
October 1998	Food was plentiful. Rabbits moved into the area. Add 15 brown beans.	Foxes had larger litters than usual. Add 2 white beans.
April 1999	Disease killed many rabbits. Remove 8 brown beans.	Food supply was low due to disease among the rabbits. Some foxes left the area. Remove 3 white beans.
October 1999	Spring came early. Rabbits could breed earlier. Add 12 brown beans.	Food was plentiful. Foxes moved into the area. Add 8 white beans.
April 2000	No change in population.	Inadequate food to feed the increased fox population. Some foxes moved out. Remove 4 white beans.
October 2000	The farm was opened to hunters, who killed pheasants. Foxes ate more rabbits. Remove 14 brown beans.	Hunters shot some foxes. Remove 2 white beans.

Name _____ Date _____ Class _____

Laboratory Activity 2 (continued)

Table 3

Date	Rabbits (brown beans)		Foxes (white beans)	
	Observed	Total	Observed	Total
October 1997				
April 1998				
October 1998				
April 1999				
October 1999				
April 2000				
October 2000				
April 2001				
October 2001				

Figure 1

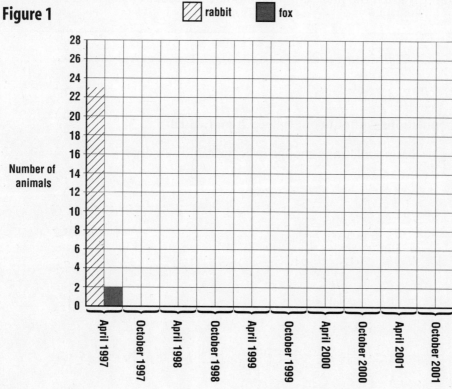

Number of animals

Laboratory Activity 2 (continued)

Questions and Conclusions

1. In this example, which animal is the predator and which is the prey?

   _____

2. How did the data from your sampling in Part A compare with those of the two biologists in April 1997?

   _____

3. Give two factors that caused a decrease in the rabbit population.

   _____

4. Give two factors that caused an increase in the rabbit population.

   _____

   _____

5. Give three factors that caused a decrease in the fox population.

   _____

   _____

6. Give three factors that caused an increase in the fox population.

   _____

   _____

7. What happened to the rabbits when the pheasant population decreased?

   _____

   _____

Strategy Check

_____ Can you sample populations without counting each individual?

_____ Can you demonstrate that populations change over time and seasons?

The Rain Shadow Effect

Chapter **5**

Interstate Highway 80 runs from San Francisco on the Pacific Ocean eastward across the Sierra Nevada mountain range and into Nevada, as shown by the map in Figure 2 at the back of this activity. The Sierra Nevada range extends north and south about 640 kilometers through eastern California.

When warm, moist air from the Pacific Ocean moves in over the western coast of the United States, it moves eastward and rises as it moves over mountain ranges. This rising causes the water vapor in the air to cool and condense to form clouds. These clouds serve as a source of precipitation in the form or rain or snow. The majority of this precipitation will fall on only one side of the mountain range. The opposite, dryer side of the mountain range is said to be in the "rain shadow" of the mountains. In this activity, you will analyze weather data to determine the effect of mountain ranges on precipitation patterns.

Strategy

You will plot elevation and precipitation data for various locations along Interstate Highway 80 on a graph.

You will infer the effect of a mountain range on the amount of precipitation received in different locations.

Materials

colored pencils

Procedure

1. Study Table 1 in the Data and Observations section and the map at the end of this activity. Table 1 lists data from eleven cities or towns along Interstate Highway 80. They are referred to as reporting stations because they are places where the National Oceanographic and Atmospheric Administration (NOAA) collects data on weather conditions, including precipitation.

2. Use the data in the table to plot a graph of the elevation of each reporting station along the highway. The grid for your graph is provided in Figure 1 in the Data and Observations section. Mark the elevation of each station above its location with a dot. Then connect the dots with a line. The resulting graph will give you a rough idea of the shape of the land as you travel along Highway 80.

3. Refer back to Table 1 and use the precipitation ranges in Table 2 to mark off regions of average precipitation on the x-axis of your graph. (Note: There may be more than one station contained within a particular region, or range of precipitation, and changes from one region, or range of precipitation, to another may occur in the areas between stations.) Using your marks as a guide, shade the area between your graph line and the x-axis with the appropriate color from Table 2 for each region, or range of precipitation. Note: The resulting graph will look something like a rainbow under your graph line. Notice that each color represents a different range of precipitation.

Laboratory Activity 1 (continued)

Data and Observations

Table 1

Reporting Station	Elevation	Average Annual Precipitation (cm)
1 San Francisco, CA	5	61
2 Vacaville, CA	34	64
3 Auburn, CA	394	88
4 Colfax, CA	732	123
5 Baxter, CA	1129	142
6 Blue Canyon, CA	1449	174
7 Soda Springs, CA	2099	163
8 Truckee, CA	1799	83
9 Verdi, NV	1488	41
10 Reno, NV	1344	19
11 Sparks, NV	1328	21

Table 2

Amount of Precipitation	Color
0 to 25 cm	Red
26 to 75 cm	Orange
76 to 125 cm	Blue
Over 126 cm	Green

Laboratory Activity 1 (continued)

Figure 1

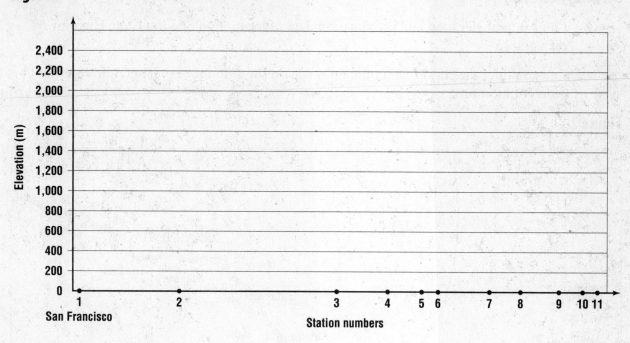

Questions and Conclusions

1. Which side of the Sierra Nevada Mountains receives the greatest amount of precipitation?
   Why?

   _____

   _____

2. Why is there more rain or snow at Baxter than at Auburn?

   _____

3. Which stations receive the greatest amounts of precipitation? Why?

   _____

   _____

4. The elevation of Reno, Nevada, is higher than the elevation of Baxter, California. Why does
   Reno receive less precipitation than Baxter does?

   _____

   _____

5. On which side of the Sierra Nevada Mountains would you expect to find environments that
   support a greater diversity and number of organisms? Why?

   _____

   _____

Laboratory Activity 1 (continued)

Strategy Check

_____ Can you plot elevation and precipitation data of locations along Interstate Highway 80 on a graph?

_____ Can you infer the effect of a mountain range on the amount of precipitation received in different locations?

Figure 2

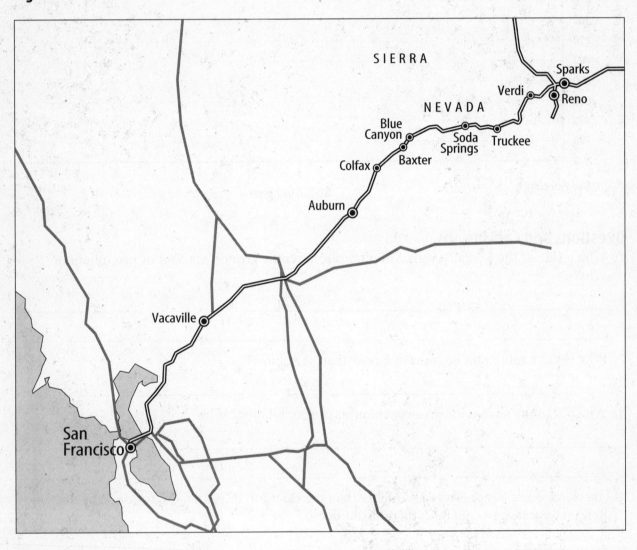

Carbon Dioxide and Earth's Temperatures

Since the Industrial Revolution in the 1800s, humans have burned greater and greater amounts of fossil fuels in order to produce more energy. As the burning of fossil fuels increases, so does the amount of carbon dioxide released into the atmosphere. Historical data from ice cores and modern data from the Mauna Loa Observatory in Hawaii show that carbon dioxide levels in the atmosphere have increased 30 percent since 1860. Growing evidence suggests that increases in atmospheric carbon dioxide may contribute to an increase in average temperatures on Earth. In this activity, you will examine the effects of an increased level of carbon dioxide, produced by fizzing antacid tablets, on air temperature.

Strategy

You will measure the air temperatures in two air samples containing different amounts of carbon dioxide.

You will graph the air-temperature data and compare the graphs.

You will infer how an increased level of carbon dioxide could affect temperatures in Earth's atmosphere.

Materials 🥽 ⚗️ 💧

graduated cylinder or metric measuring cup
2 clear-plastic cups
water
2 clear-plastic boxes with lids
masking tape
marking pen
2 thermometers
6 fizzing antacid tablets
sunlight or bright lamp
clock with second hand or timer
2 different colors of pencils or pens

Procedure

1. Using a graduated cylinder, measure and pour 100 mL of water into each of the two plastic cups.
2. Set one cup in the center of each plastic box.
3. Use masking tape and a marking pen to label one of the boxes *A* and the other *B*.
4. Place one thermometer in each of the boxes. Put the lids on the boxes. Check to make sure you can read the thermometers when looking into the boxes through the lids. If necessary, reposition the thermometers. Be sure the thermometers are located in the same positions in both boxes.

Laboratory Activity 2 (continued)

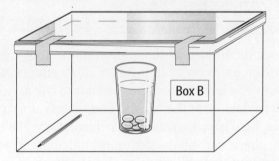

5. Remove the lids from both boxes.

6. Place the lid on Box A and seal it with tape.

7. Add six antacid tablets to the water in the plastic cup in Box B. Immediately place the lid on the box and seal the lid to the box with masking tape. Observe what happens in the cup.

8. Being careful not to disturb the contents of the boxes, place both boxes, side by side, in an area where they will receive bright sunlight. If that is not possible, place both boxes the same distance from a single, bright light source.

9. Once the boxes are in place, begin taking temperature readings. Measure the temperatures in both boxes every minute for 20 minutes. Record the temperatures in the table in the Data and Observations section.

10. After you have collected your data, plot your data from Box A on the graph in the Data and Observations section. Then plot your data from Box B on the same graph with a different color of pencil or pen.

Laboratory Activity 2 (continued)

Data and Observations

Time (min)	Temperature in Box A (°C)	Temperature in Box B (°C)
1		
2		
3		
4		
5		
6		
7		
8		
9		
10		
11		
12		
13		
14		
15		
16		
17		
18		
19		
20		

Laboratory Activity 2 (continued)

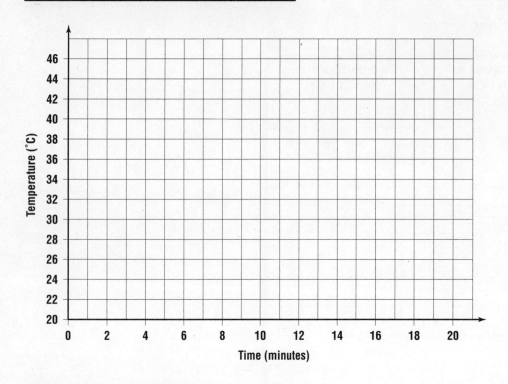

Questions and Conclusions

1. What evidence did you have that carbon dioxide was being released into the air in one of the boxes?

   _____

   _____

2. Was there any difference in the graphs of the air temperature in the two boxes? If so, describe it.

   _____

   _____

3. What can you infer about how increased levels of carbon dioxide might affect average temperatures in Earth's atmosphere?

   _____

   _____

Strategy Check

_____ Can you measure the air temperatures in two air samples containing different amounts of carbon dioxide?

_____ Can you graph the air-temperature data and compare the graphs?

_____ Can you infer how an increased level of carbon dioxide could affect temperatures in Earth's atmosphere?

Succession Communities and Grasses

Chapter 6

Once lichens and other pioneer species die and organic matter is added to the soil, other plants are able to grow. Grasses are a characteristic species of primary and secondary succession. They are tough and adaptable, grow quickly and readily, and further enrich the soil when they die.

Strategy

You will observe the effect of sunlight and water on the growth of grass.

You will identify differences between the characteristics of a succession community and the characteristics of a climax community.

Materials

four small plastic pots filled with soil and planted with grass seed
permanent marker
small box open only at one end
water

Procedure

1. Label the pots 1, 2, 3, and 4.
2. Place pot 1 in a location that will receive a lot of indirect sunlight.
3. Cover pot 2 with the box. Place it next to pot 1.
4. Water pots 1 and 2 with the same amount of water twice a week. Keep the soil moist but not wet.
5. Place pots 3 and 4 in the same location as plants 1 and 2.
6. Water pot 3 daily. Keep the soil wet.
7. Do not water pot 4.
8. In the Data and Observations table, write a hypothesis describing how you think the amount of light will affect pots 1 and 2. Write another hypothesis describing how you think the amount of water will affect pots 1, 3, and 4.
9. Care for the plants daily for three weeks. Record observations at the end of each week.

Data and Observations

Hypothesis			
Plants 1 and 2 (light)			
Plants 1, 3 and 4 (water)			
Observations			
Plant	Week 1	Week 2	Week 3
1			
2			
3			
4			

Laboratory Activity 1 (continued)

Questions and Conclusions

1. What was the effect of the amount of light on pots 1 and 2? How does your hypothesis differ from the results?

_____

_____

_____

_____

2. What was the effect of the amount of water on pots 1, 3, and 4? How does your hypothesis differ from the results?

_____

_____

_____

3. What characteristics of grass do you think make it well-suited as a late primary or secondary succession plant?

_____

_____

_____

4. Would you find grasses in a climax community? Why or why not?

_____

_____

_____

_____

_____

Strategy Check

_____ Can you observe the effect of sunlight and water on the growth of grass?

_____ Can you identify differences between the characteristics of succession and climax communities?

Exploring Life in Pond Water

Looking through a microscope, you can see a miniature world of many, many microorganisms. In a single drop of pond water, you might be able to see protists, bacteria, plants, and tiny animals. Because the ecosystem of a pond is not uniform throughout, different organisms live in different parts of the pond. Water collected from the surface and from near the sediment will contain some of the same organisms, but there will be some organisms that live in only one area or the other.

Strategy

You will examine two samples of pond water under the microscope.
You will identify some of the organisms that exist in each sample of pond water.
You will compare the organisms found near the surface to those found near the bottom of the pond.

Materials

water collected from the surface of a pond
droppers (2)
microscope slides (2)
coverslips (2)
microscope
water collected near the bottom of a pond

Procedure

1. Use the dropper to place one drop of surface pond water on a clean microscope slide. Carefully put the coverslip on the drop.
2. Examine the surface pond water under low and high power magnification of the microscope. Carefully move the slide so that you are able to examine all areas of the slide.
3. Use the drawings in the Data and Observations section to identify the organisms you observe. On the lines under the drawings, indicate which organisms were observed in the surface pond water.

4. Repeat steps 1 through 3 for a drop of water from the bottom of the pond.
5. Complete Table 1 in the Data and Observations section by entering the microorganisms that you observe in the water from the surface and the bottom of the pond.
6. Enter your data in the table your teacher has prepared on the board by putting a mark by each organism that you observed in your samples. When all students have entered their data, complete Table 2 by summarizing the data from the table on the board.

Laboratory Activity 2 (continued)

Data and Observations

1. *Oscillatoria*

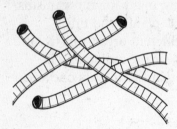

2. *Paramecium*

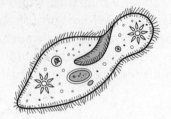

3. *Vorticella*

4. *Daphnia* (waterflea)

5. *Euglena*

6. *Amoeba*

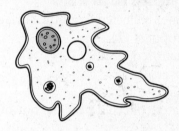

7. Rotifers

8. Nematodes

9. *Cyclops*

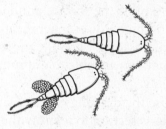

10. Diatoms

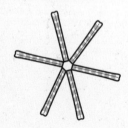

11. *Volvox*

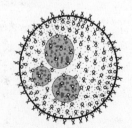

12. Desmids

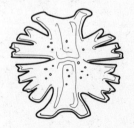

Laboratory Activity 2 (continued)

Table 1

Individual Data	
Organisms found in surface pond water	**Organisms found near pond bottom**

Table 2

Group Data		
Organism	**Near surface**	**Near bottom**
Oscillatoria		
Paramecium		
Vorticella		
Daphnia		
Euglena		
Amoeba		
Rotifers		
Nematodes		
Cyclops		
Diatoms		
Volvox		
Desmids		

Laboratory Activity 2 (continued)

Questions and Conclusions

1. Did you find different organisms in the surface and deep pond water samples? Explain.

_____

_____

2. What factors might influence why some organisms are found only in surface pond water or only in deep pond water?

_____

_____

3. Because a pond is an ecosystem that changes all the time, experimental variables might have an impact on your observations. Explain how each of the following might influence the organisms observed:
   a. season of the year

_____

   b. delay between when the sample was collected and the experiment was performed

_____

   c. depth of collection site for water from the bottom of the pond

_____

   d. distance from shore that the surface water was collected

_____

4. In what ways might human activity impact the pond water ecosystem?

_____

_____

_____

Strategy Check

_____ Can you examine samples of pond water under the microscope?

_____ Can you identify the organisms that exist in each sample of pond water?

_____ Can you compare the organisms found on the surface of a pond to those found near the bottom?

Paleogeographic Mapping

Paleo- means old as in paleontology, the study of old life (fossils). *Geo-* means Earth, as in geology, the study of Earth. *Graphic* refers to a drawing or painting. Therefore, paleogeographic could be translated as "Old Earth Picture." Scientists often use fossil evidence to help them develop a picture of how Earth was long ago. By examining and dating rock formations and fossils of various plants and animals, scientists are able to formulate hypotheses about what Earth's surface might have looked like during a particular period in history. For example, similar rock formations and certain types of plant and animal fossils of a particular age could indicate whether two, now separate, land areas might have been connected during that period. Further analysis of the samples and data could also provide clues to the climate of that area or whether it was dry land or covered by an ocean. To classify events in the geologic past, scientists have divided the millions of years of Earth's history into segments, called *eras*. In this activity, you will examine evidence from the fossil record relative to a current map of an imaginary continent and develop a map of what the continent and the surrounding area might have looked like during the Mesozoic Era (248 million to 65 million years ago).

Strategy

You will determine how fossil evidence can be used to infer information about a continent during the geologic past.

You will interpret fossil evidence to draw a map showing how a continent appeared during the Mesozoic Era.

Materials

colored pencils or markers

Procedure

1. Figure 1 shows a map of a present-day imaginary continent. Locations *A* through *I* are places where fossils have been found in rocks dating to the Mesozoic Era. Study the map and look at the fossils key below the map.

2. From the locations of the different fossils, infer where the land areas were at the time the fossil organisms lived. Keep in mind that the way the modern continent looks may have no relationship to where the land/ocean boundaries were during the Mesozoic Era.

3. Use one color of pencil or marker to color in the land areas on the map in Figure 1. Fill in the block labeled Land with the same color. Use a different color of pencil or marker to color in the ocean areas on the map in Figure 1. Fill in the block labeled Ocean with this color.

4. In the space provided under Data and Observations, draw a map showing land and water areas during the Mesozoic Era. Use the color boundaries you added to Figure 1 as your guideline. Based on these boundaries, add all of the symbols from the map key in Figure 1 to your map.

5. Color all the areas around and between the labeled areas on your map as either land or ocean. Fill in the blocks labeled Land and Ocean with the colors you used.

Laboratory Activity 1 (continued)

Figure 1

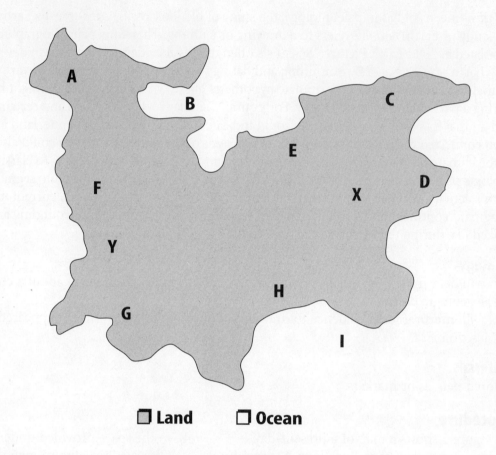

☐ **Land**   ☐ **Ocean**

Fossils found in Mesozoic rocks

A (shark teeth)   F (teeth/bones of small mammals)

B (petrified wood)   G (dinosaur bones)

C (sea stars)   H (corals)

D (leaf and fern imprints)   I (dinosaur footprints)

E (seashell fragments)

X, Y (Areas to be identified after completing your map)

Laboratory Activity 1 (continued)

Data and Observations

Mesozoic Map

☐ **Land**   ☐ **Ocean**

Questions and Conclusions

1. According to your map, was location Y land or water during the Mesozoic Era? Explain how you decided.

   _____

   _____

2. According to your map, was location X land or water during the Mesozoic Era? Explain how you decided.

   _____

3. Compare your map with those of other students. Why do you think that not everyone agreed on whether location X was land or water? How could you find out which interpretation was correct?

   _____

   _____

   _____

Laboratory Activity 1 (continued)

4. Corals grow only in warm, shallow oceans near the coastlines of continents that are relatively near the equator. Would knowing this fact make you revise your map? Why or why not?

_____

_____

_____

5. Suppose the modern continent shown in Figure 1 was located in an area that is extremely cold. Using the evidence you have, plus the information in Question 4, what could you infer about the continent?

_____

_____

_____

Strategy Check

_____ Can you determine how fossil evidence can be used to infer information about a continent during the geologic past?

_____ Can you interpret fossil evidence to draw a map showing how a continent appeared during the Mesozoic Era?

LAB 2 Laboratory Activity

How do continental plates move?

One of the models that helps explain how tectonic plates move is the convection model. In this hypothesis, the molten magma of the mantle boils like water in a pot. The pattern of the moving water forms a circular wave or current as hot water rises to the top and cooler surface water is forced to the side of the pot and back down to be heated again. Inside the Earth it is believed there are many convection cells, or regions in the mantle, that boil like this. The different cells have their own currents and constantly move independently of one another. The crust of the Earth has a much lighter mass and density than the magma. As a result, the plates of crust are moved by convection currents and broken up on the boiling surface of the mantle.

Strategy

You will model convection currents and the movement of tectonic plates.
You will predict what will happen to tectonic plates at the margins of convection cells.

Materials

hot plate   scissors   tongs
water   medium to large–mouthed pot
sheets of plastic foam wrap for padding packages (not made from corn or organic materials)

Procedure

1. The hot plates should be turned on high. Carefully fill the pot 2/3 full of water and place it on the hot plate. It will take a while for the water to boil.

2. Obtain a piece of flat plastic foam wrap. Use scissors to cut several shapes that represent tectonic plates. If you are working in a group you may mark your tectonic plates with a pencil or pen if you wish so that you can recognize it when the water boils.

3. Carefully place your pieces of foam on the surface of the water. If the water has any steam or tiny bubbles at the bottom of the pan, ask your teacher to place the foam in the pot for you.

4. As the water heats, watch the action of the bubbles as they rise from the bottom of the pot. Observe everything you can about what happens to them when they rise under a piece of foam. Record your observation in the table provided.

5. Once the water begins to boil, watch your pieces of foam. How do they move? In what direction do they go? Do they stay in one place in the pot or do they move ? Do they crash into other pieces of foam?

Record the answers to these observations in the data table. Be sure to observe the boiling pot for a while. It may first seem there is no pattern to the action in the pot, but careful observation will reveal certain movements in the boiling water.

Figure 1

Foam

Laboratory Activity 2 (continued)

6. When the experiment is over, your teacher will turn off the hot plates and remove the foam with tongs for cooling. DO NOT remove the pieces yourself. They will cool quickly. When they are cooled, find your pieces and return to your lab station or seat.

7. In your data table write down any observed changes in your foam. Does it still have water in it? Have any of the corners been melted or damaged? Write down any other observations in your table.

Data and Observations

Action of bubbles	1.
Movement of foam pieces in boiling water	2.
Condition of foam after experiment	3.

Questions and Conclusions

1. How did you describe what happened to the bubbles as they gathered under the foam? What happened at the sides of the foam?

_____

_____

_____

Laboratory Activity 2 (continued)

2. What type of natural feature is similar to the action of the bubbles? Explain your answer.

_____

_____

_____

3. Describe the movement of the plastic pieces when the water started to boil. Could you see a pattern?

_____

_____

_____

4. How does this experiment model the moving tectonic plates?

_____

_____

5. How is this experiment different from the real world in terms of tectonic plates? (Hint: What were your foam pieces like after the experiment?)

_____

_____

_____

6. Predict what would happen if the convection currents of the molten magma changed direction or stopped altogether?

_____

_____

_____

Strategy Check

_____ Can you model convection currents and the movement of tectonic plates?

_____ Can you predict what will happen to tectonic plates at the margins of convection cells?

Wave Detecting

Today, scientists use seismographs to observe and record seismic waves. Before the nineteenth century, however, scientists used other types of instruments to study earthquakes. These instruments did not record seismic waves. Instead, they indicated the magnitude or direction of an earthquake in a general way. In the 1600s in Italy, for example, scientists used a device that contained water to observe seismic waves. The amount of water spilling out during an earthquake indicated the amount of shaking. In this lab, you will make a simple earthquake-detecting device and determine how it is affected by seismic waves.

Strategy

You will model and observe the effects of seismic waves.
You will infer how the energy released by an earthquake affects the amplitude, or height, of seismic waves.

Materials

baking pan
large ceramic or stainless steel bowl
pitcher of tap water
dropper
meterstick
textbook
paper towels

Procedure

1. Work with a partner. Place the baking pan on a flat surface such as a desk or counter. Set the bowl inside the pan.
2. Pour water into the bowl from the pitcher. Fill the bowl to within 1 to 2 mm of the rim.
3. Using the dropper add water to the bowl until the surface of the water arches above the rim (Figure 1). This is your earthquake detector.
4. Model an earthquake by having a partner drop a textbook near the detector from a height of 2 cm. Observe what happens to the water in the bowl. Do waves appear? Does water spill over? Record your observation in the Data and Observations section. Add more water to the bowl with the dropper if any spills out. Then repeat this step, switching roles with your partner.

5. Repeat step 4 several more times. Each time, you should increase the height at which you drop the book by several centimeters.
6. If any water spills outside the baking pan, be sure to wipe it up with the paper towels.

Figure 1

Water

Laboratory Activity 1 (continued)

Data and Observations

Table 1

Trial	Height from Which Book Is Dropped (cm)	Observations of Earthquake Detector
1		
2		
3		
4		

Questions and Conclusions

1. How are the waves produced by the book landing on the table similar to seismic waves?

_____

_____

2. Could you tell that the waves produced by some of your model earthquakes had greater amplitude than others? Explain.

_____

_____

3. How did you increase the magnitude of your model earthquake? How did increasing the magnitude of the earthquake affect the amplitude of the waves in your detector?

_____

_____

4. How could you use two earthquake detectors to model how the amplitude of seismic waves is affected by the distance the waves travel? Explain.

_____

_____

_____

Strategy Check

_____ Can you model and observe the effects of seismic waves?

_____ Can you infer how the energy released by an earthquake affects the amplitude of seismic waves?

Volcanic Eruptions

Some volcanic eruptions consist of violent explosions of gases and tephra, while others involve a relatively quiet flow of lava around a vent. The type of eruption that occurs depends on both the composition of the magma and the amount of gas trapped in it. Thick magma that is rich in silica tends to trap steam and other gases. The more gas in the magma, the greater the pressure that builds up in the volcano. The tremendous pressure that builds in silica-rich magma is released when the volcano erupts explosively.

By contrast, magma that contains less silica tends to be less explosive and flow more easily. This type of magma is rich in iron and magnesium and traps smaller amounts of gas. It produces basaltic lava that flows from a volcano in broad, flat layers. In this lab, you will model both basaltic lava flows and explosive eruptions.

Strategy

You will model and observe how the buildup of pressure in a volcano can lead to an explosive eruption.

You will determine how layers of basaltic lava accumulate.

Materials 🥽 🔨 🧤

newspaper	old paintbrushes (3)
balloons (9)	sponge
empty coffee can	marker
measuring cup	meterstick
plaster of paris	scissors
water	piece of thick cardboard (approximately 50 cm × 50 cm)
1 lb. plastic margarine tubs (2)	textbooks
red, blue, and green food coloring	small tubes of toothpaste in different colors
wooden paint stirrers (3)	(white, green, striped)

WARNING: *Never put anything you use in a laboratory experiment into your mouth.*

Procedure

Part A—Modeling Explosive Eruptions

1. Work in a group of five or six students. Put on your apron and goggles, and cover your work area with sheets of newspaper.

2. Inflate six of the balloons. Put less air in some of the balloons than in others. You'll need two small balloons, two medium, and two large. Leave the remaining balloons uninflated.

3. In the coffee can, combine 1 L of plaster mix with 2 L of water. Stir the mixture with a wooden stirrer until the mixture is smooth. You should use a bit more water than the directions on the box suggest. Thinner plaster will be easier to work with.

4. Pour about one-third of the mixture into each of the plastic tubs, leaving the final third in the can. Add several drops of food coloring to each container, and stir.

You should end up with three colors of plaster: red, green, and blue. Do this step as quickly as possible since the plaster mix will begin to harden.

5. Using paintbrushes, coat the entire surface of each of the inflated balloons with a thin layer of plaster. Paint the two small balloons blue, the medium balloons green, and the large balloons red. Using any color, paint a band around the center of each of the empty balloons, leaving the ends unpainted (Figure 1). Set the balloons on sheets of newspaper to dry. If you spill any plaster while you are painting, wipe it up with a damp sponge.

Laboratory Activity 2 (continued)

Figure 1

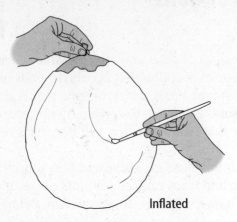

Inflated

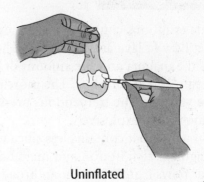

Uninflated

6. While the plaster is drying, skip to Part B of the procedure.

7. To model the buildup of pressure inside magma, try to inflate the empty balloons. What do you observe? Record your observation in the Data and Observations section.

8. Spread newspapers on an open area of the floor. With the marker, draw a large X on the center of the paper. To model an explosive eruption, take one of the small, blue balloons and place it on the X. Pop the balloon by stepping on it. Leave the pieces of the plaster in place and pop the second small balloon in the same way. **WARNING:** *Wear your safety goggles throughout this experiment.*

9. With the meterstick, measure the distance from the X to the piece of plaster that landed the farthest from it. This distance represents the radius of the debris field. Record this measurement in Table 1 the Data and Observations section.

10. Repeat step 8 using the medium balloons. Measure and record the distance from the X to the piece of *green* plaster that landed farthest from it.

11. Repeat step 8 using the large balloons. Measure and record the distance from the X to the piece of *red* plaster that landed farthest from it.

Part B—Modeling Basaltic Lava Flows

1. Use the scissors to poke a hole near the center of the piece of cardboard. Widen the hole until it is just large enough for the cap of a tube of toothpaste to fit through it.

2. Make two stacks of books and place the cardboard on top of them so that the hole is suspended about 30 cm above your work surface (Figure 2).

3. Remove the cap from one of the tubes of toothpaste. Stick the cap end of the tube through the hole so that the tube is upright and just the mouth is sticking out the top of the cardboard. Model a basaltic lava flow by slowly squeezing out the contents of the tube.

Figure 2

4. Measure the height and diameter of your "lava" flow and record your measurements in Table 2 in the Data and Observations section.

5. To model additional eruptions, repeat steps 3 and 4 using the other two tubes of toothpaste to add to your "lava" flow.

6. Return to step 7 of Part A.

Laboratory Activity 2 (continued)

Data and Observations
What did you observe when you inflated the plaster-coated balloons?

_____

Table 1

Balloon Size	Radius of Debris Field (cm)
Small 1	
Small 2	
Medium 1	
Medium 2	
Large 1	
Large 2	

Table 2

Eruption	Diameter (cm)	Height (cm)
1		
2		
3		

Questions and Conclusions

1. The air in your balloons modeled the gases that build up in silica-rich magma. Which balloons (small, medium, or large) modeled magma under the greatest pressure? Explain.

   _____

   _____

2. What do your results from Part A tell you about the relationship between pressure and the force of an explosive volcanic eruption?

   _____

   _____

3. What type or types of volcano did you model in Part A? Explain your answer.

   _____

   _____

Laboratory Activity 2 (continued)

4. What were you modeling when you inflated the plaster-coated balloons in step 7 of Part A?

_____

_____

5. a. In Part B, how did the layers of toothpaste accumulate? Did the second and third layers form on top of the first layer or beneath it?

_____

_____

b. What does this result tell you about the age of the top layer of basaltic lava on a volcano compared with lower layers?

_____

_____

6. How did the height of the volcano you modeled in Part B compare with its width? What type of volcano has this shape?

_____

_____

7. How did the two types of eruptions you modeled differ from one another? How were they alike?

_____

_____

_____

Strategy Check

_____ Can you model an explosive eruption due to the buildup of gas pressure?

_____ Can you describe how layers of basaltic lava accumulate?

Principle of Superposition

LAB
1 Laboratory Activity

The principle of superposition states that beds in a series are laid down with the oldest at the bottom and successively younger layers on top. Beds may be exposed at the surface as a result of folding and uplifting or because of faulting. If part, or all, of a layer is removed by erosion and this surface is covered by a new deposit, the contact is called an unconformity. In some areas, river erosion will cut deeply enough to expose a number of layers, such as in the Grand Canyon.

Strategy

You will construct a map legend.
You will construct a block diagram of an area.
You will write the geologic history of the area.

Materials

block diagram, Figure 1
glue or paste
cardboard, thin
pencils (colored)
scissors
tape (clear)

Procedure

1. Set up a legend for your diagram and select a color for each layer. Record the legend in Table 1.
2. Glue Figure 1 on the cardboard. Color the map according to your legend.
3. Cut out, fold, and tape the block diagram as instructed on Figure 1.

Data and Observations

Table 1

	Color
Layer A	
Layer B	
Layer C	
Layer D	

Questions and Conclusions

1. Which layer is oldest? Explain.

_____

_____

_____

2. What kind of structure do the layers have?

_____

_____

_____

Laboratory Activity 1 (continued)

3. Why is the glacial till not folded?

_____

_____

_____

4. What does the presence of the peat and soil layer in the glacial till tell you?

_____

_____

_____

5. Was this a mountainous area prior to glaciation? Explain.

_____

_____

_____

_____

_____

6. How many advances of the ice occurred here?

_____

7. Write the geologic history of the area illustrated in the block diagram.

_____

_____

_____

_____

_____

_____

_____

Strategy Check

_____ Can you set up a map legend?

_____ Can you construct a block diagram?

_____ Can you write the geologic history of the area illustrated by a block diagram?

Laboratory Activity 1 (continued)

Figure 1

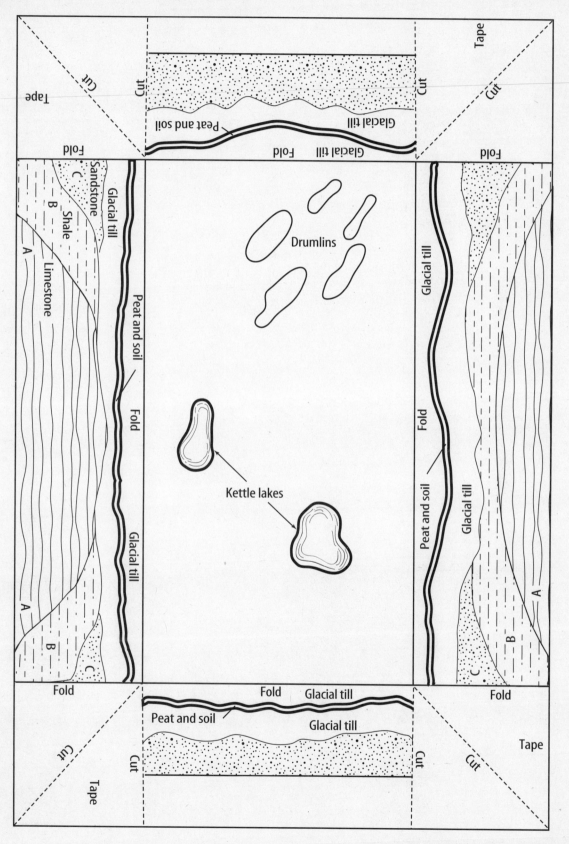

Index Fossils

Fossils found in the deepest layer of undisturbed rocks in an area represent the oldest forms of life in that particular rock formation. When reading Earth history, these layers would be "read" from bottom to top, or oldest to most recent. If a specific fossil is typically found only in a particular type of rock and is found in many places worldwide, the fossil might be useful as index fossil. The index fossil can be useful in determining the age of layers of rock or soil. By comparing this type of information from rock formations in various parts of the world, scientists have been able to establish the geologic time scale.

Strategy

You will make trace fossils from several objects.
You will distinguish between index fossils and other fossils.

Materials

newspaper
objects to use in making trace fossils (3)
clay
container, at least 25 cm × 20 cm × 15 cm (or approximately shoe-box size)
varieties of "soil" (3)
*sand
*potting soil
*pea gravel
*mulch
*shredded dried leaves
*fresh grass cuttings
small shovel
*scoop
*Alternate materials

Procedure

1. Cover your desk or table with several layers of newspaper. Select three objects to use to make your trace fossils. Label these objects A, B, and C.

2. Make trace fossils of the three objects by pressing clay onto each of them. Carefully remove the clay from the objects. Label your trace fossils A, B, and C, and set your fossils aside. Make a second trace fossil from objects A and C. Label these.

3. Choose three different types of soil. You can have different amounts of each type of soil, but together the three soils should almost fill your container.

4. Layer one type of soil into your container. Bury one trace fossil A in this layer of soil. Sketch this layer in Figure 1 in the Data and Observations section. Be sure to note the location of the fossil.

5. Repeat step 4 twice using a different type of soil for each layer. In the second layer, bury trace fossils A, B, and C. Place only trace fossil C in the third layer. Fossil B is your index fossil.

Laboratory Activity 2 (continued)

6. Choose a time period that each of your soil layers represents, and add this information to Figure 1. Consider the distribution of fossils in the layers of soil when you select the time span for each object. Also, because fossil B is your index fossil, it must represent a unique time period. Be sure that the time period you select for the middle layer does not overlap with the other time spans.

7. Exchange containers with another group. Tell the group when object B, your index fossil, existed.

8. Carefully excavate your new container. Sketch each layer in Figure 2 as you proceed with the excavation. Carefully note where each fossil is found. Compare your sketches with the sketches made by the group who made the container.

9. Based on the age of the index fossil, determine what you can know about a time line for the second container. Add details on what you can tell about the time line to Figure 2.

Data and Observations

Figure 1—First Container

Layer	Bottom	Middle	Top
Time period			
Sketch			

Figure 2—Excavated Container

Layer	Bottom	Middle	Top
Time period			
Sketch			

Laboratory Activity 2 (continued)

Questions and Conclusions

1. Explain why an index fossil must represent a unique time period.

   _____

   _____

2. Are the three fossils in the middle layer from the same time period?

   _____

   _____

3. Is fossil A in the deepest layer from the same type of organism as fossil A in the middle layer?

   _____

   _____

4. Are the two fossils from object A from the same time period? What do you know about the duration of organism A in the geologic time line?

   _____

   _____

   _____

5. What is important to note while you are excavating?

   _____

   _____

6. Compare your sketch of the container you excavated with the sketch made by the makers of that container? Explain any important differences.

   _____

   _____

7. Explain how an index fossil is used to determine the age of surrounding fossils.

   _____

   _____

   _____

   _____

   _____

Strategy Check

_____ Can you make trace fossils from a variety of objects?

_____ Can you determine the index fossil in the excavation?

Differences in a Species

Chapter 10

To use fossil dating efficiently, paleontologists first separate fossils into groups. The most useful group for classification is called a species. A species is a population of individuals that have similar characteristics. Small differences in individuals might result in the development of a new species by a series of gradual changes. These changes can be traced from one geologic time division to another if the fossil record is good.

Strategy

You will describe the variations present within a species.
You will describe a species in terms of one characteristic.

Materials

meterstick   graph paper   pencils (colored)

Procedure

1. The species you will study is *Homo sapiens,* or yourself. You and your classmates are all members of this species. Remember that all living things grow at different rates. It is possible that you will find some big differences in your study, but everyone still belongs to the same species.
2. Record all characteristics of the species that you can. Record which of the characteristics you could measure and compare for all members of the species.

3. Measure and record in Table 1 the height of yourself and each of your classmates. Round off the height to the nearest tenth of a meter (0.1 m).
4. Measure the heights of a class of younger students. Record this data in Table 2.

Data and Observations

1. Characteristics: _____

_____

Table 1

Name	Height (m)	Name	Height (m)	Name	Height (m)

Laboratory Activity 1 (continued)

Table 2

Name	Height (m)	Name	Height (m)	Name	Height (m)

Use a separate sheet of paper to graph the Frequency (number of persons having the same height) on the vertical axis against the Height (m) on the horizontal axis. Use one color for your own class and a second color for the younger class.

Questions and Conclusions

1. On what characteristics can you classify this group as a single species?

_____

2. Where do most of the members of your class fall in regard to height?

_____

3. Where do most of the members of the younger class fall in regard to height?

_____

4. What change has taken place over time?

_____

5. How is this activity like fossil dating?

_____

_____

6. How is this activity different from fossil dating? (Hint: Think in terms of the time spans involved.)

_____

_____

Strategy Check

_____ Can you describe the variations present within a species?

_____ Can you describe a species in terms of a range of a characteristic?

Looking at the Geologic Time Scale

As you have learned, Earth's history can be divided in geologic time segments called eras, periods, and epochs. These time periods are useful for placing events such as the disappearance of the dinosaurs and the appearance of humans in perspective relative to the history of life on Earth. The time segments are not as equal as they sound, however. In earlier eras, life processes on Earth appear to have been developing quite slowly, whereas later eras saw enormous changes over relatively short segments of geologic time. In this Laboratory Activity you will compare and contrast various segments of Earth's history by constructing a geologic time line.

Strategy

You will make a graph to compare the durations of Earth's geologic eras.

You will measure and construct a time line that shows Earth's geologic eras.

You will identify time relationships among events in Earth's geologic history.

You will record and illustrate significant events during the Mesozoic and Cenozoic Eras on a time line.

Materials

4–4.5 m of adding machine tape
meter stick
colored pencils

Procedure

Part A

1. Figure 1 shows approximately how long ago each major division of Earth's geologic time scale began. Use the information to calculate how long each of these divisions lasted. Record that information in the last column of Figure 1.

2. Using that information, make a bar graph on the grid in the Data and Observations section to show how long each division lasted.

Part B

3. You will use a piece of adding machine tape to make a geologic time line. Distance will represent time, with 1 cm representing 10 million years.

4. Using the meter stick, draw a straight line through the middle of the tape from one end to the other.

5. Starting at the left end of the tape, measure a distance that represents the length of Precambrian Time. Refer back to the time duration you calculated in Figure 1. Make a vertical line at the correct point.

To the left of that line label the division on your time line *Precambrian Time.*

6. From that vertical line, measure a distance that represents the length of the Paleozoic Era. Refer back to the time duration you calculated in Figure 1. Make a vertical line at the correct point. To the left of that line, label the division on your time line *Paleozoic Era.*

7. Repeat step 6 for the Mesozoic Era and the Cenozoic Era.

8. Lightly color each division on your time line a different color.

9. Divide the Mesozoic Era and the Cenozoic Era into the Periods and Epochs shown in Figure 2.

10. Then, using information from your text (such as the mass extinction) and the additional information in Figure 2, mark in the correct positions on your time line for significant events that occurred during the Mesozoic and Paleozoic Eras. Illustrate each of these events with a small drawing.

Laboratory Activity 2 (continued)

Data and Observations

Figure 1

Major geologic time division	When time division began	Length of time division lasted
Precambrian time	4.0 billion years ago	
Paleozoic era	544 million years ago	
Mesozoic era	245 million years ago	
Cenozoic era	65 million years ago	

Figure 2

Division	Time period (millions of years ago)	Event(s)
Triassic period	248–213	breakup of Pangaea
Jurassic period	213–145	first birds
Cretaceous period	145–65	Rocky Mountains form; first flowering plants
Paleocene epoch	65–55.5	first hooved mammals
Eocene epoch	55.5–33.7	first whales
Oligocene epoch	33.7–23.8	early formation of European Alps
Miocene epoch	23.8–5.3	first dogs and bears
Pliocene epoch	5.3–1.8	first Ice Age; first hominoids
Pleistocene epoch	1.8–0.008	modern humans
Holocene epoch	0.0008–present	Sea levels rose as climate warmed; first civilizations

Laboratory Activity 2 (continued)

Graph

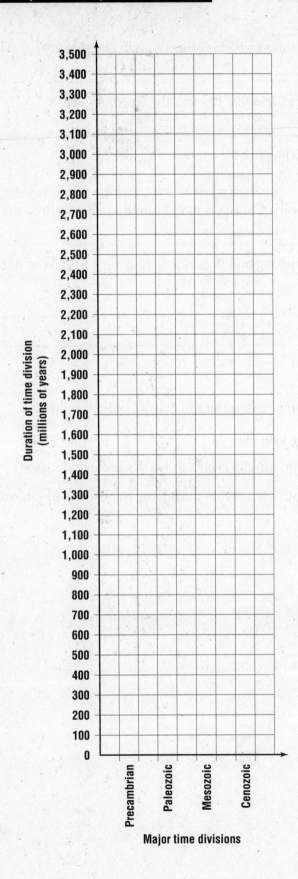

Laboratory Activity 2 (continued)

Questions and Conclusions

1. Based on your graph in Part A, which time division is the longest? The shortest?

_____

2. About how many times longer than the Mesozoic Era was the Paleozoic Era?

_____

3. In which era do you live today? In which epoch?

_____

4. About how many times longer than modern humans have hooved mammals lived on Earth?

_____

5. What problems did you have in constructing and illustrating your time line? Why did you have those problems?

_____

_____

Strategy Check

_____ Can you make a graph to compare the durations of Earth's geologic eras?

_____ Can you measure and construct a time line that shows Earth's geologic eras?

_____ Can you identify time relationships among events in Earth's geologic history?

_____ Can you record and illustrate significant events during the Mesozoic and Cenozoic Eras on a time line?

Earth's Spin

Chapter 11

The speed at which Earth turns on its axis can be described in two ways. The velocity of rotation refers to the rate at which Earth turns on its axis. Velocity of rotation refers to Earth as a whole. For any point on Earth's surface, the speed of Earth's rotation can be described as its instantaneous linear velocity. This velocity is the speed of the point as it follows a circular path around Earth.

Strategy

You will determine the instantaneous linear velocity of some points on Earth.
You will compare the linear velocities of points at different locations on Earth.

Materials

globe (mounted on axis)   meterstick
tape (adhesive)   stopwatch
string

Procedure

Part A

1. Place small pieces of adhesive tape on the globe along the Prime Meridian at the equator, at 30° N latitude, at 60° N latitude, and at the North Pole.
2. Line up the tape with the metal circle above the globe; see Figure 1.
3. With your finger on the globe, move it west to east for one second; see Figure 2.
4. For each location marked by tape, measure the distance from the Prime Meridian to the metal circle. Use the string and the meterstick to get accurate distances.

Record the distances in Table 1.
5. Realign the metal circle with the pieces of tape. Move the globe west to east for 2 s. Record the distances from the tapes to the metal circle in Table 1.
6. Repeat step 5, moving the globe for 3 s. Record your results in Table 1.

Part B

Calculate the speed of each point for each trial. Record the speeds in Table 2. Use the formula:
velocity (cm/s) = distance (cm)/time (s)

Figure 1   North Pole

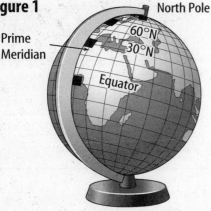

Figure 2   North Pole

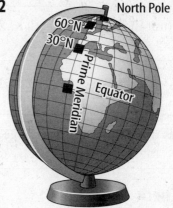

Laboratory Activity 1 (continued)

Data and Observations

Table 1

Latitude	Distance (cm)		
	1 s	2 s	3 s
Equator			
30° N			
60° N			
North Pole			

Table 2

Latitude	Velocity (cm/s)		
	Trial 1	Trial 2	Trial 3
Equator			
30° N			
60° N			
North Pole			

Questions and Conclusions

1. Which point moved the farthest distance in all three trials?

_____

2. Which point moved the least distance in all three trials?

_____

3. Which point did not move at all in the three trials?

_____

4. On what does the linear velocity of a point depend?

_____

5. How does the linear velocity change as you move from the equator to the poles?

_____

Strategy Check

_____ Can you determine instantaneous linear velocity?

_____ Can you see that the linear velocity is not the same for all points on Earth?

Earth's Shape

You've probably seen photographs of Earth taken by satellites in space. Such photographs clearly show Earth's round shape. Early astronomers didn't have spacecraft to help them study Earth. They had to rely on observation and measurement. In this activity, you'll explore some methods used by early astronomers to determine Earth's true shape.

Strategy

You will demonstrate evidence of Earth's shape.
You will describe the type of shadow cast by Earth during a lunar eclipse.

Materials

small piece of cardboard
scissors
basketball
flashlight
textbook

Procedure

1. Cut out a triangular piece of cardboard so that each side measures approximately 6 cm.
2. Hold a basketball at eye level about 33 cm from your eye. Have your partner slowly move the cardboard up and over the basketball from the opposite side.
3. In the space below, sketch the cardboard as it appears when the top of the cardboard first comes in sight over the basketball.

Make another sketch of the cardboard as it appears when fully visible above the basketball.

4. Darken the room. Use a flashlight to cast a shadow of a textbook against the wall. Do the same for the basketball. In the space below, draw the shadows of the textbook and the basketball.

Data and Observations

Laboratory Activity 2 (continued)

Questions and Conclusions

1. Compare and contrast your two drawings of the cardboard.

_____

_____

_____

2. How were your different views of the cardboard similar to the view of a ship on the horizon approaching shore?

_____

_____

3. How did the cardboard activity demonstrate evidence of Earth's shape?

_____

_____

_____

4. Compare and contrast your drawings of the shadows cast by the basketball and the textbook.

_____

_____

5. During a lunar eclipse, Earth casts a shadow on the Moon. What type of shadow would Earth cast if it were flat? What type of shadow does Earth cast on the Moon during a lunar eclipse?

_____

_____

6. How do the shadows you observed demonstrate evidence of Earth's shape?

_____

_____

_____

7. Can you think of any other evidence that demonstrates Earth's round shape? Describe this evidence.

_____

Strategy Check

_____ Can you demonstrate evidence of Earth's shape?

_____ Can you describe the type of shadow cast by Earth during a lunar eclipse?

Venus—The Greenhouse Effect

Because Venus is closer to the Sun, it receives almost twice the amount of solar radiation received by Earth. However, because of its clouds Venus reflects more radiation in to space than does Earth. We might expect Venus, therefore, to have surface temperatures similar to Earth's. However, the Pioneer vehicles to Venus have measured surface temperatures of 460°C. Some scientists explain this high temperature as the "greenhouse effect." When the solar energy strikes the surface of Venus, the energy is absorbed and changed into heat energy. This heat energy is reflected back to the atmosphere where it is trapped.

Strategy

You will build a model to show the greenhouse effect.
You will compare this model to Earth.
You will form a hypothesis about temperatures on Venus using data collected from this model and from the *Pioneer* spacecraft.

Materials

soil
clear plastic storage box and lid
cardboard (stiff)

thermometer
heat lamp (mounted)
watch

graph paper
pencils (colored)

Figure 1

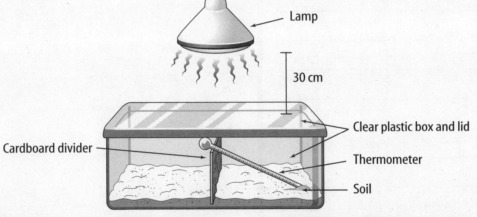

Procedure

1. Place about 3 cm of soil in the bottom of the clear plastic box.
2. Thoroughly moisten the soil with water.
3. Cut the piece of cardboard so that it makes a divider for the box. The cardboard should not quite reach the top of the box. Insert the divider into the box.
4. Lean the thermometer against the divider with the bulb end up. (See Figure 1) Put the lid on the box.
5. Position the box and lamp in an area of the room where no direct sunlight reaches. **WARNING:** *Use care handling heat lamp.*

6. Place the heat lamp about 30 cm above the box and direct the light so it shines on the thermometer bulb.
7. Turn off the lamp and allow the thermometer to return to room temperature. Record room temperature under Data and Observations.
8. Turn on the lamp and measure the temperature every minute for 20 min. Record the temperatures in Table 1.
9. Turn off the lamp and allow the thermometer to return to room temperature. Remoisten the soil and repeat step 8 without the lid. Record your data in Table 1.

Laboratory Activity 1 (continued)

Data and Observations

Room temperature: _____

Table 1

Time (min)	Temperature (°C) Lid On	Lid Off
1		
2		
3		
4		
5		
6		
7		
8		
9		
10		
11		
12		
13		
14		
15		
16		
17		
18		
19		
20		

On a separate piece of paper, graph the data using two different colors. Plot Temperature on the vertical axis and Time on the horizontal axis.

Laboratory Activity 1 (continued)

Questions and Conclusions

1. Did the temperature increase the most with the lid on or off? Why?

   _____

   _____

   _____

2. Draw a diagram of Earth showing its atmosphere and what occurs due to solar radiation in the atmosphere. List the components of Earth's atmosphere on your diagram. Write a brief explanation of the greenhouse effect on Earth.

   _____

   _____

   _____

   _____

3. Compare the greenhouse effect of the activity to the greenhouse effect on Earth. How are they similar? How are they different?

   _____

   _____

   _____

   _____

Laboratory Activity 1 (continued)

4. Venus's atmosphere is composed mainly of carbon dioxide, carbon monoxide, water, nitrogen, and sulfuric acid. Venus's atmosphere is 100 times more dense than Earth's atmosphere. From the surface of Venus up to 20 km, there appears to be a clear region of atmosphere. A thick layer of clouds extends from about 50 km to 80 km above the surface of Venus. These clouds are composed of drops of sulfuric acid. Above and below these clouds are other, thinner layers of haze. Venus's ionosphere extends from 100 km to 200 km above the surface. Like the ionosphere of Earth, it has layers. The temperature in the ionosphere of Venus is cooler than the temperature in Earth's ionosphere.

    Draw a diagram of Venus showing its atmosphere and what happens to solar radiation in the atmosphere. List the components of Venus's atmosphere on your diagram. Write a brief explanation of the greenhouse effect on Venus.

_____

_____

_____

_____

5. Compare the greenhouse effect on Earth and Venus. Can you think of a reason why the surface of Venus is so much hotter than the surface of Earth?

_____

_____

_____

_____

Strategy Check

_____ Can you build a model to show the greenhouse effect?

_____ Can you compare this model to Earth?

The Behavior of Comets

LAB 2 Laboratory Activity

Chapter 12

One way scientists study the behavior and composition of comets is by observing them as they orbit the Sun. Observations made through telescopes and pictures sent back by space probes have led scientists to believe a comet is a mixture of ice and rock. Heat from the Sun vaporizes some of the comet's ice, which releases bits of rock and dust that form a cloud around the comet. Solar winds blowing on the cloud create the comet's tail. The intensity of the solar wind makes the tail point away from the Sun, no matter which direction the comet is facing. Because the comet is vaporizing when it becomes visible from Earth, each time we see a comet, we are witnessing its deterioration.

Strategy

You will model and observe the behavior of comets orbiting the Sun.
You will describe the behavior and draw inferences about the life of a comet based on your observations.

Materials

newspaper
small electric fan
books or boxes
waxed paper
ruler

red, green, or blue construction paper
    (the color should make water drops easy to see)
sand (not dirt)
ice (crushed, not in cubes)

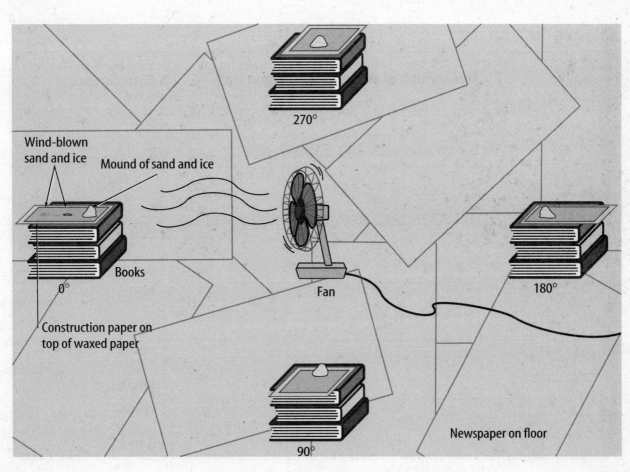

Laboratory Activity 2 (continued)

Procedure

1. Working in groups of four students, place newspaper on your lab table or the floor near an electric outlet. Put the fan in the middle of the newspaper. Place books or boxes at four positions around the fan. The first position should be 0° The next are at 90°, 180°, and 270°. Be sure to cover books with wax paper to protect them against any water spills.

2. Take a piece of colored construction paper about 23 cm × 15 cm and place it with its longer edge away from the fan. Do this for each position. See Figure 1. Then get a small mixture (about a tablespoon) of sand and ice and mound it on the paper at the end nearest the fan. Draw a line on the page around the mound of sand and ice.

3. Have one student carefully turn on the fan at the 0° position and observe the effect the blowing wind has on the ice/sand mixture.

Let the fan run for three minutes and then turn it off. Record your observation in the table provided.

4. Turn the fan so that it is pointing to the 90° position and repeat the procedure. Continue until the fan has run on all four positions and then repeat for position 0°. Turn the fan to the 90° position. Carefully turn on the fan one more time. Be sure to record all your observations in the table.

5. When you are finished, take your paper and carefully place it on the ground or tabletop. Try not to move any of the particles as you move the paper. Take your ruler and measure the distance the water drops and sand moved from their original position at the front of the paper. Record these distances in the last column of the table.

Data and Observations

Fan Position (deg.)	Description of Behavior of Ice and Sand	Distance of Particle Distribution (cm)
1. 0°		
2. 90°		
3. 180°		Water: Sand:
4. 270°		Water: Sand:
5. 0° Second trial		Water: Sand:
6. 90° Second trial		Water: Sand:

Laboratory Activity 2 (continued)

Questions and Conclusions

1. What is one behavior of the ice and sand you observed?

_____

_____

_____

2. How would you explain what you saw?

_____

_____

_____

3. How does this behavior demonstrate the similarities between your experiment and what we observe in a comet orbiting the Sun?

_____

_____

_____

4. Where does the water and dust from a melting comet go?

_____

_____

5. Using your answer from question 4, would you expect a comet to always die out? Explain your answer.

_____

_____

_____

Strategy Check

_____ Can you model the behavior of a comet orbiting the Sun?

_____ Can you describe this behavior based on what you know about the composition of comets?

Absolute and Apparent Magnitudes

Chapter 13

The apparent magnitude of a star, or how much light is received on Earth, can be confusing to an astronomer trying to measure the distance a star is from Earth. Apparent magnitude is much different from the absolute magnitude, which is the true measure of how much light the star emits. These two variables control the brightness of the stars we see in our night sky. The absolute magnitude is not the same for every star. It is determined by the amount of light it gives off. The second variable is the amount of light received on Earth. The mixing of these two variables can lead to misunderstanding about the size and distance of a star. That is why it is important to understand the characteristics of stars and light to be able to correctly determine what we see in the night sky.

Strategy

You will observe how light behaves over distance.
You will predict how two stars that are different in size and far away from each other may appear in the night sky.

Materials

black construction paper
scissors
small flashlight

rubber bands
medium sized nail
tape

measuring tape or meterstick
white correction fluid
*chalk
* markers
* Alternate materials

Procedure

1. Students will work in groups of three to four. Use your scissors to cut a piece of black construction paper large enough to comfortably cover the light end of the flashlight.

2. Cover the end of the flashlight with the paper and secure it in place with a rubber band. Take the sharp end of the nail and carefully poke a single hole in the center of the paper covering. The smaller the hole the better.

3. Find a wall or hard surface on which you can tape a background of more black construction paper. An area about one meter square would be best for the experiment. An alternate choice would be to use the black- or white-board in the classroom. If you do use a wall, write only with the appropriate materials, such as chalk or erasable marker.

4. At a distance of two meters or six feet from the wall, mark a spot with tape on the ground. Then mark the next interval at 1.3 meters or four feet. The last mark is at 0.6 meters or two feet.

Figure 1

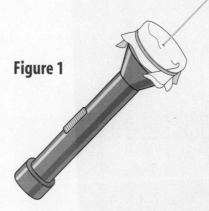

5. Ask your instructor to darken the room as much as possible. One student will stand at the six foot mark and turn on the flashlight. The other students will mark the edges of the diameter of the circle of light made by the flashlight with correction fluid, chalk, or markers. Be sure to notice the intensity of the inner and outer regions of the circle of light. You will record this in the data table provided.

Laboratory Activity 1 (continued)

6. Repeat this procedure at the closer interval. Then repeat one more time at the closest interval. Look at the intensity of the light instead. When is it most intense and where is it very diffuse? Record these observations in your table.

7. Observe the behavior of light at different intervals. Try to account for what you observe by what you know. For instance, you know the amount of light exiting the flashlight has not changed at all during the experiment. So what is happening to the dispersal of light? Record your hypothesis in the space marked "Hypothesis for the dispersal of light."

Data and Observations

Table 1

Diameter of Light Circle (cm)			Observations about Intensity of Light (cm)
Trial 1	Trial 2	Trial 3	

Laboratory Activity 1 (continued)

According to your experiment, your circle of light changed in size as you got closer to the wall. The intensity, or brightness, also changed. How would you account for this? Write your hypothesis in the space below.

Hypothesis for the dispersal of light: _____

_____

_____

_____

Questions and Conclusions

1. The circle of light produced by your flashlight on the wall was larger when you were farther away from the wall. Was the light more or less intense? How do you account for this?

_____

_____

_____

_____

2. The circle of light got smaller as you approached the wall. Was the light more or less intense? How do you account for this?

_____

_____

_____

_____

3. As a result of your experiment, would you expect a star to appear brighter when closer to or farther from the Earth? Explain your answer.

_____

_____

_____

_____

4. If you used a bigger and brighter flashlight and repeated the same experiment, what would you expect your results to be like? Explain your answer.

_____

_____

_____

_____

Laboratory Activity 1 (continued)

5. Suppose you were going to perform the experiment with two students: One holds a weak flashlight; the other a strong flashlight. How would you place the students so that the circles of light on the wall were exactly the same size? Explain your answer in terms of magnitude.

_____

_____

_____

_____

6. How would you model the difference in absolute magnitude between the two flashlights?

_____

_____

_____

_____

7. Predict what an astronomer would look for if he or she wanted to determine the size and heat of a star and its distance from the Earth. Would it be a good idea to watch the star over a long period?

_____

_____

_____

_____

Strategy Check

_____ Can you observe how light behaves over distance?

_____ Can you predict how two stars that are different in size and far away from each other may appear in the night sky?

Spectral Analysis

LAB
2 Laboratory
Activity

The photograph of the spectrum of a star, sorted by color across a plate, will reveal spectral lines upon close examination. The lines are produced by elements in a star at high temperature. These lines represent the chemical composition of the star. Each element has its own "fingerprint." To analyze the spectra of stars, scientists collected spectra of all the known elements. If we compare the spectral lines of an unknown star with the spectral lines of elements, we can determine the chemical composition of the star. More recently, we have discovered not only the composition of the stars but also their temperatures, their rotational rate, and their relative motion with regard to Earth.

Strategy

You will construct a simple spectral analyzer.
You will determine the composition of a star using the spectral analyzer.
You will determine other characteristics of a star by comparing the spectral lines with a standard.

Materials

scissors

Procedure

1. Turn to the third page of this lab. Cut out the pull tab card; the spectroscope fingerprints card; and Stars B, C, and D along the dashed lines.
2. Make five slits along the dashed lines A, B, C, D, and E on the fingerprints card.
3. From left to right, insert "Pull Tab Out" up through slit E, down through slit D, up through slit C, down through slit B, and up through slit A.

4. Compare the lines of each known element with the lines of Star A. If lines match, then that element is present in Star A. Record your findings in Table 1.
5. Star B, Star C, and Star D are provided for further study and comparison. Each can be placed over Star A.

Data and Observations

Table 1

Star	Chemical Composition	Other Characteristics
A		
B		
C		
D		

Laboratory Activity 2 (continued)

Questions and Conclusions

1. When you hear someone say that neon lights look beautiful, what color comes to mind? What color is suggested by the "fingerprints" of neon?

_____

_____

_____

_____

2. Did any of the stars have the same chemical composition? Look at the table.

_____

_____

_____

3. Sometimes scientists see spectral lines that do not fit the usual pattern. The lines might be shifted from their usual positions. This may suggest that the star is moving either toward the observer (shift toward the blue) or away from the observer (shift toward the red). Look at the spectral lines for Star B and Star D. Star B is the standard for comparison. How is Star D different? What is a possible explanation for the difference?

_____

_____

_____

_____

4. If the scientist sees the spectral lines wider than usual, he or she relates this spectral broadening to either rotational speed (the broader the faster), temperature (the broader the hotter), or pressure (the broader the greater pressure). Look at the spectral lines for Star B and Star C. Star B is the standard. How is Star C different? What could be a possible explanation?

_____

_____

_____

_____

Strategy Check

_____ Can you construct a simple spectral analyzer?

_____ Can you determine the composition of a star using the spectral analyzer?

_____ Can you determine other characteristics of a star by comparing the spectral lines with a standard?

Laboratory Activity 2 (continued)

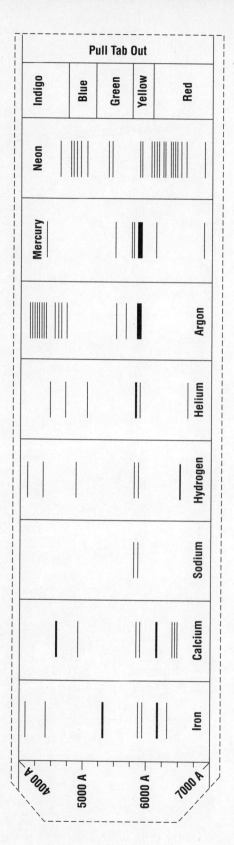

Pull Tab Out

| Indigo | Blue | Green | Yellow | Red |

Neon

Mercury

Argon

Helium

Hydrogen

Sodium

Calcium

Iron

4000 A   5000 A   6000 A   7000 A

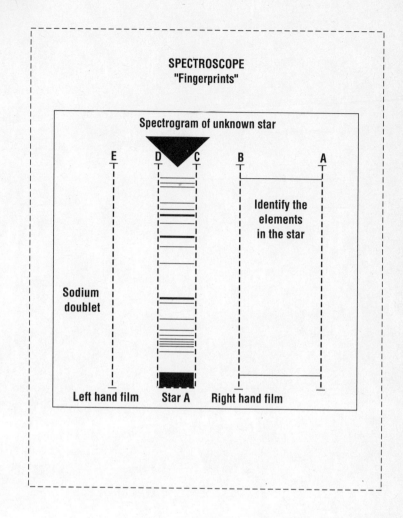

SPECTROSCOPE
"Fingerprints"

Spectrogram of unknown star

E   D   C   B   A

Identify the
elements
in the star

Sodium
doublet

Left hand film   Star A   Right hand film

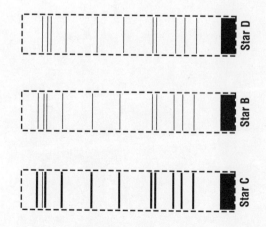

Star D

Star B

Star C

Atoms—Smaller Than You Think!

Chapter 14

Have you ever seen an atom? Unless you've been lucky enough to look through a very powerful microscope, you haven't seen anything close in size to an atom. Matter is composed of atoms, and atoms are everywhere. You can't see atoms or even molecules. They are too small. But even though you can't see an atom with your own eyes, you can use other senses to detect the presence of some of the small molecules made from atoms. In this experiment, you will study the small size of vanilla molecules.

Strategy

You will predict what happens when drops of a liquid that is made up of small molecules are placed in a balloon.

You will observe some aspects of small molecules.

Materials

rubber balloon   dropper
closet or locker   vanilla extract (2 mL)

Procedure

1. Use a dropper to place 20 to 40 drops of vanilla extract into a rubber balloon. (See Figure 1)
2. Blow up the balloon, and tie it tightly.
3. Place the balloon in a small, enclosed area such as a closet or locker for at least 30 minutes.
4. What do you think will happen to the molecules of vanilla extract in the balloon? Record your predictions in the table in the Data and Observations section.
5. After 30 minutes, open the closet or locker. What did you observe? Record your observation in the Data and Observations section.

Figure 1

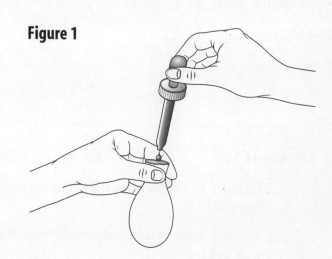

Data and Observations

Predictions	Observations
1.	2.

Copyright © Glencoe/McGraw-Hill, a division of The McGraw-Hill Companies, Inc.

Laboratory Activity 1 (continued)

Questions and Conclusions

1. How do you explain the results of this experiment?

_____

_____

_____

_____

2. What can you infer from your results about the size of the vanilla molecules?

_____

_____

3. What does the fact that helium-filled balloons deflate tell you about the size of helium atoms?

_____

_____

4. Helium gas is made up only of helium atoms. Vanilla molecules have the formula $C_8H_8O_3$. Which do you think will leak more rapidly from equally inflated balloons—helium or vanilla? Use the size of the molecules to explain your answer.

_____

_____

_____

_____

Strategy Check

_____ Can you detect the presence of atoms and molecules that are very small with any sense but sight?

_____ Can you infer anything about the sizes of different molecules and atoms based on how they behave?

Isotopes and Atomic Mass

Elements as they occur in nature are mixtures of isotopes. All the isotopes of any given element have the same number of protons, but each isotope has a different number of neutrons. Most elements have more than one isotope. Therefore, the atomic masses of elements that are included in the periodic table are average atomic masses. In this exercise, you will use a model of isotopes to help you understand the concept of average atomic mass.

Strategy

You will model isotopes of two different elements using candy-coated peanuts and candy-coated chocolate in two colors.

You will determine the average mass of the two colors of candy-coated peanuts and candy-coated chocolate.

You will relate your results to the average atomic mass of elements.

Materials

4 red and 3 green candy-coated peanuts
4 red and 3 green candy-coated chocolates

Procedure

1. Group together four red candy-coated peanuts and two red candy-coated chocolates. The two different kinds of candy represent two isotopes of the same element.

2. Assume that a red peanut has a mass of 2 candy units, and a red chocolate has a mass of 1 candy unit. Calculate the average mass of the red candy as follows:

   a. Calculate the total mass of red peanuts by multiplying the number of red peanuts by the mass of one peanut candy.

   b. Calculate the total mass of red chocolates by multiplying the number of red chocolates by the mass of one chocolate candy.

   c. Add these two total masses together and divide by the total number of candies.

3. Repeat step 2 using three green peanuts and three green chocolates. Assume a green peanut has a mass of 4 units and a green chocolate has a mass of 3 units.

4. Record your calculations in the table in the Data and Observations section.

Data and Observations

	Mass of peanuts (number of candies × mass of 1 unit)	Mass of Chocolates (number of candies × mass of 1 unit)	Average mass $\left(\dfrac{\text{total mass}}{\text{total number of candies}}\right)$
Red			
Green			

Laboratory Activity 2 (continued)

Questions and Conclusions

1. There were six red and six green candies. Why were their calculated average masses different?

_____

_____

2. Calculate the average mass of Y in a sample of element Y that contains 100 atoms of Y-12 and 10 atoms of Y-14.

3. Look at the atomic masses of elements in the periodic table. Notice that none of the atomic masses of naturally abundant elements are whole numbers. Use your candy model of atoms to explain this.

_____

_____

_____

4. Uranium is an element used in most nuclear reactors. Its two major isotopes are U-235 and U-238. Look up the mass of uranium on the periodic table. Infer which isotope is the most common, and explain why you came to this conclusion.

_____

_____

5. Compare and contrast mass number and average atomic mass.

_____

_____

_____

6. Hydrogen has three isotopes. The most common one, protium, has no neutrons. Deuterium, the second isotope, has one neutron. Tritium has two neutrons. Using this information, calculate the mass number of these isotopes.

_____

_____

Strategy Check

_____ Can you explain how candy-coated peanuts and candy-coated chocolate can be used as a model for isotopes?

_____ Are you able to find the average mass of an element?

Relationships Among Elements

The periodic table is a wonderful source of information about all of the elements scientists have discovered. In this activity, you will investigate the relationship among the elements' atomic numbers, radii, and positions in the periodic table.

An atom's atomic radius is the distance from the center of the nucleus to the edge of the atom. The radii for elements with atomic numbers from 3 through 38 are given in Table 1. The radii are so small that a very small metric unit called a picometer is used. A picometer (pm) is one trillionth of a meter.

Strategy

You will plot the atomic radii of elements with atomic numbers 3 through 38.
You will examine the graph for repeated patterns.

Materials

copy of the periodic table   graph paper   pencil

Table 1

Name and symbol		Atomic number	Atomic radius (picometers)	Name and symbol		Atomic number	Atomic radius (picometers)
Aluminum	Al	13	143	Magnesium	Mg	12	160
Argon	Ar	18	191	Manganese	Mn	25	127
Arsenic	As	33	121	Neon	Ne	10	131
Beryllium	Be	4	112	Nickel	Ni	28	124
Boron	B	5	85	Nitrogen	N	7	71
Bromine	Br	35	117	Oxygen	O	8	60
Calcium	Ca	20	197	Phosphorus	P	15	109
Carbon	C	6	77	Potassium	K	19	231
Chlorine	Cl	17	91	Rubidium	Rb	37	248
Chromium	Cr	24	128	Scandium	Sc	21	162
Cobalt	Co	27	125	Selenium	Se	34	119
Copper	Cu	29	128	Silicon	Si	14	118
Fluorine	F	9	69	Sodium	Na	11	186
Gallium	Ga	31	134	Strontium	Sr	38	215
Germanium	Ge	32	123	Sulfur	S	16	103
Iron	Fe	26	126	Titanium	Ti	22	147
Krypton	Kr	36	201	Vanadium	V	23	134
Lithium	Li	3	156	Zinc	Zn	30	134

Laboratory Activity 1 (continued)

Procedure

1. On the graph paper, label the horizontal axis with the numbers 0 through 38 to represent the atomic numbers of the elements you will be plotting.

2. Label the vertical axis by tens with numbers from 0 through 280. These numbers represent atomic radii.

3. Plot the atomic radius for each of the elements with atomic numbers 3 through 38.

Questions and Conclusions

1. Look at the shape of your graph. What patterns do you observe?

_____

2. What family is represented by the high peaks in your graph? _____

3. What family is represented by the low points in your graph? _____

4. What family is represented by the smaller peaks just before the high peaks? _____

5. What do you notice about the radii of the elements at the high peaks as you move from left to right on your graph? Look at your periodic table and find the element that represents each high peak. What does each high peak begin in the periodic table?

_____

_____

6. What happens to the radii of the elements between two highest peaks? What does each of these groups of elements represent?

_____

_____

7. How can a graph such as the one you made help to predict the properties of elements that have not been discovered yet?

_____

_____

_____

_____

8. How do the radii of metals in each period compare with the radii of nonmetals in that period?

_____

Strategy Check

_____ Can you plot a graph of the atomic radii of elements?

_____ Can you observe repeating patterns in the graph?

Periodicity

A periodic event is one that occurs time after time in a regular, predictable way. If you have a table of repeating events, you can use it to predict what might be true in the future. For example, astronomers are able to predict the appearance of a comet if they know the dates of the comet's appearance in the past. A calendar is a good model for the periodic table of the elements.

Strategy

You will determine missing information on the calendar for a month.
You will make predictions about future and past events based on the calendar.

Procedure

1. Label the seven columns of the calendar page in Figure 1 with the numbers 1 through 7. There are seven families, or groups, in this periodic table. They are the days of the week.

2. Label the five rows of the calendar page with the numbers 1 through 5. There are five periods in this periodic table. Each period is a week.

3. Notice that some information is missing. Fill in the missing information by examining the information in the blocks surrounding the spots where the missing information belongs.

Data and Observations

Figure 1

SUN	MON	TUE	WED	THUR	FRI	SAT
				1	2	3 Soccer practice
4	5	6	7	8	9	10
11	12	@	#	15	16	17 Soccer practice
18	19	20	21	22	23	24
25	26	27	28	29	30 Your Birthday	31

Laboratory Activity 2 (continued)

Questions and Conclusions

1. Two of the days in Families 3 and 4 are marked with an @ and a #. What dates should go in these positions?

_____

2. Family 5 doesn't have a name. What is the correct name for this family?

_____

3. What dates are included in the third period of the table?

_____

4. Assuming that the previous month had 30 days, what day of the week would the 28th of that month have been?

_____

5. What period of this table would it appear in?

_____

6. Notice that two dates have been scheduled for regular soccer practice. When would you expect the next two soccer practices to take place?

_____

7. The following month will start on the day after the 31st. What day of the week will it be?

_____

8. Suppose your birthday occurs on the 30th of the month. Explain how your birthday is a periodic event.

_____

Strategy Check

_____ Can you provide missing information in a periodic table if you have information about the neighboring blocks?

_____ Can you make predictions based upon information in a periodic table?

LAB 1 Laboratory Activity

Chemical Bonds

An ion is an atom that is no longer neutral because it has gained or lost electrons. One important property of ions is the ability to conduct electricity in solution.

Ions can form in solution in several ways. Ionic compounds, which are often compounds created from metals of Groups 1 and 2 and nonmetals in Groups 16 and 17, dissolve in water to form ions. Acids and bases also form ions in solution. Although acids and bases contain covalent bonds (bonds in which electrons are shared), acids form the hydronium ion (H_3O^+), while bases form the hydroxide ion (OH^-) in water.

Other covalent compounds form solutions, too. These solutions, however, do not conduct an electric current because they do not form ions in solution. A measure of how well a solution can carry an electric current is called conductivity.

Strategy

You will determine the conductivity of several solutions.

You will classify the compounds that were dissolved in the solutions as ionic compounds or covalent compounds.

Materials

9-V battery and battery clip
tape
cardboard sheet, 10 cm × 10 cm
alligator clips (4)
LED (light-emitting diode)
resistor, 1,000-Ω
copper wire, insulated, 20-cm lengths (2)
microplate, 24-well
pipettes, plastic (7)
sulfuric acid solution, $0.1M$ H_2SO_4
sodium chloride solution, $0.1M$ NaCl
sodium hydroxide solution, $0.1M$ NaOH
sucrose solution, $0.1M$ sucrose
glucose solution, $0.1M$ glucose
sugar cubes (sucrose)
sodium chloride (rock, crystalline)
water, distilled
paper towels
WARNING: *Sulfuric acid and sodium hydroxide can cause burns. Avoid contacting them with your skin or clothing. Do not taste, eat, or drink any materials used in the lab.*

Procedure

Part A—Constructing a Conductivity Tester

1. After putting your apron and goggles on, attach the 9-V battery clip to the 9-V battery. Use tape to attach the battery securely to the cardboard sheet, as shown in Figure 1.

2. Attach an alligator clip to one of the lead wires of the 1,000-Ω resistor. Connect the alligator clip to the *red* lead wire of the battery clip. Tape the resistor and alligator clip to the cardboard sheet as shown in Figure 2. **WARNING:** *Use care when handling sharp objects.*

3. Attach an alligator clip to the *long* lead wire of the LED. Connect this alligator clip to the second wire of the 1,000-Ω resistor. Tape the alligator clip to the cardboard sheet.

4. Attach an alligator clip to the *short* lead wire of the LED. Connect this clip to one end of one of the insulated copper wires. Tape the clip to the cardboard sheet as shown in Figure 3.

5. Attach the last alligator clip to one end of the second insulated copper wire. Connect the alligator clip to the *black* lead wire of the battery clip. Tape the alligator clip to the cardboard sheet as shown in Figure 4.

6. Check to be certain that the alligator clips, resistor, and battery are securely taped to the cardboard sheet and that the clips are not touching one another.

Laboratory Activity 1 (continued)

7. Have your teacher check your conductivity tester.

8. Touch the two ends of the two insulated wires and observe that the LED glows.

Figure 1

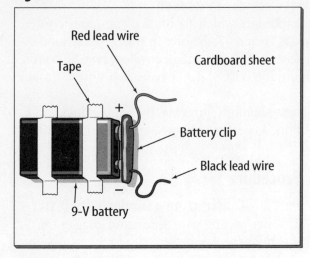

Red lead wire

Tape

Cardboard sheet

Battery clip

Black lead wire

9-V battery

Figure 3

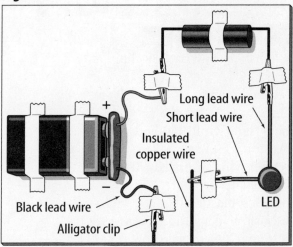

Alligator clip

Long lead wire

Short lead wire

LED

Insulated copper wire

Alligator clip

Figure 2

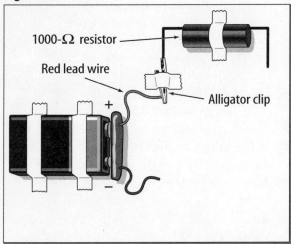

1000-Ω resistor

Red lead wire

Alligator clip

Figure 4

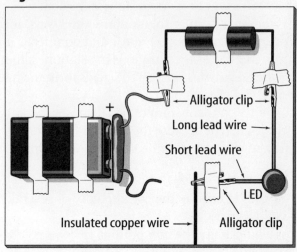

Long lead wire

Short lead wire

Insulated copper wire

Black lead wire

Alligator clip

LED

Laboratory Activity 1 (continued)

Figure 5

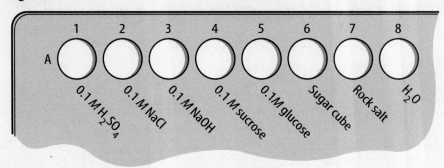

Part B—Testing the Conductivity of a Solution

1. Place the microplate on a flat surface. Have the numbered columns of the microplate at the top and the lettered rows at the left. **WARNING:** *Wash hands immediately after coming in contact with any of the prepared solutions. Inform your teacher if you come in contact with any chemicals.*

2. Using a clean pipette, add a pipette of the sulfuric acid solution to well A1.

3. Using another clean pipette, add a pipette of the sodium chloride solution to well A2.

4. Repeat step 3 for each remaining solution. Use a clean pipette for each solution. Add the sodium hydroxide solution to well A3, the sucrose solution to well A4, the glucose solution to well A5, a sugar cube to well A6, and a piece of rock salt to well A7.

5. Using a clean pipette, add a pipette of distilled water to well A8. For steps 1–5 see Figure 5.

6. Place the exposed ends of the two insulated copper wires into the solution in well A1, positioning the wires so they are at opposite sides of the well. Be sure that the exposed ends of the wire are completely submerged.

7. Observe the LED. Use the brightness of the LED as an indication of the conductivity of the solution. Rate the conductivity of the solution using the following symbols: + (good conductivity); − (fair conductivity); or 0 (no conductivity). Record your rating in the corresponding well of the microplate shown in Figure 6.

8. Remove the wires and dry the ends of the wires with a paper towel.

9. Repeat steps 6, 7, and 8 for each remaining well in the microplate.

Data and Observations

Figure 6

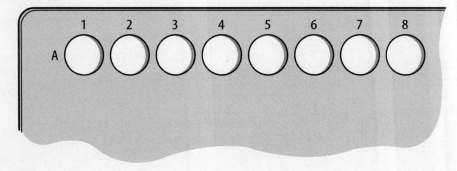

Laboratory Activity 1 (continued)

Questions and Conclusions

1. What is the conductivity of distilled water?

_____

2. Why was the conductivity of the distilled water measured?

_____

_____

_____

3. After studying your results, infer which solutions contained ions. Which solutions did not contain ions?

_____

_____

4. Which solutions contained covalent compounds? Did any of these solutions conduct an electric current?

_____

_____

_____

5. Did the crystal of table salt or the sugar cube conduct electricity?

_____

_____

6. How did the conductivities of the crystal of table salt and the $0.1 M$ NaCl solution compare?

_____

_____

7. From your results, describe one property of ions in solution.

_____

_____

Strategy Check

_____ Can you test the conductivity of a solution?

_____ Can you distinguish between a solution that contains ions and one that does not?

Chemical Activity

The atoms of most chemical elements either gain or lose electrons during reactions. Elements whose atoms lose electrons during reactions are classified as metals. Metals are found on the left side of the periodic table of elements. The tendency of an element to react chemically is called activity. The activity of a metal is a measure of how easily the metal's atoms lose electrons.

Strategy

You will observe chemical reactions between metals and solutions containing ions of metals.
You will compare the activities of different metals.
You will rank the metals in order of their activities.

Materials

microplate, 96-well
paper, white
pipette, plastic microtip
aluminum nitrate solution, $0.1M$ $Al(NO_3)_3$
water, distilled
copper nitrate solution, $0.1M$ $Cu(NO_3)_2$
iron nitrate solution, $0.1M$ $Fe(NO_3)_2$
magnesium nitrate solution, $0.1M$ $Mg(NO_3)_2$
nickel nitrate solution, $0.1M$ $Ni(NO_3)_2$
zinc nitrate, $0.1M$ $Zn(NO_3)_2$
paper towels
metal strips (8 1-mm × 10-mm strips of each: aluminum, Al; copper, Cu; iron, Fe; magnesium, Mg; nickel, Ni; and zinc, Zn)
hand lens or magnifier

WARNING: *Many of these solutions are poisonous. Avoid inhaling any vapors from the solutions. These solutions can cause stains. Do not allow them to contact your skin or clothing.*

Procedure

1. Wear an apron and goggles during this experiment.
2. Place the microplate on a piece of white paper on a flat surface. Have the numbered columns of the microplate at the top and lettered rows at the left.
3. Using the microtip pipette, place 15 drops of the aluminum nitrate solution in each of wells A1–G1. Rinse the pipette with distilled water.
4. Place 15 drops of copper nitrate solution in each of wells A2–G2 using the pipette. Rinse the pipette with distilled water.

Figure 1

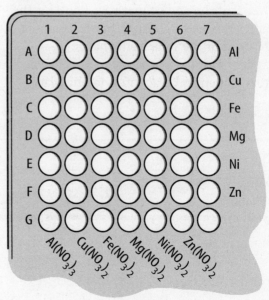

Laboratory Activity 2 (continued)

5. Repeat step 4 for each of the remaining solutions. Add the iron nitrate solution to wells A3–G3, the magnesium nitrate solution to wells A4–G4, the nickel nitrate solution to wells A5–G5, the zinc nitrate solution to wells A6–G6. Leave the wells in column 7 empty.

6. Carefully clean each metal strip with a paper towel.

7. Place one strip of aluminum in each of wells A1–A7.

8. Place one strip of copper in each of wells B1–B8.

9. Repeat step 8 for the remaining metals. Add the iron strips to wells C1–C7, the magnesium strips to wells D1–D7, the nickel strips to wells E1–E7, and the zinc strips to wells F1–F7. Do not put strips in the wells in row G.

10. Figure 1 shows the metals and the solutions that are in each of wells A1–G7.

11. Wait 10 min.

12. Use a hand lens or magnifier to observe the contents of each well. Look for a change in the color of the solution in each well by comparing it with the color of the solution in well G at the bottom of the column. Look for a change in the texture or color of the metal strip in each well by comparing it with the piece of metal in well 7 at the end of that row. Look for the appearance of deposited materials in the bottom of the well. Each change or appearance of deposits is an indication that a chemical reaction is taking place.

13. If you see an indication of a reaction, draw a positive sign (+) in the corresponding well of the microplate shown in Figure 2 in the Data and Observations section. If you see no indication of a reaction, draw a negative sign (–) in the corresponding well of Figure 2.

14. Count the number of positive signs in each row of wells in Figure 2. Record the value under the corresponding metal in Table 1.

Data and Observations

Figure 2

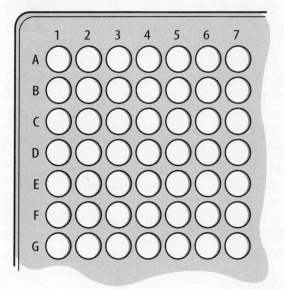

Table 1

Metal	Al	Cu	Fe	Mg	Ni	Zn
Number of reactions	1.	2.	3.	4.	5.	6.

Laboratory Activity 2 (continued)

Questions and Conclusions

1. Why were solutions but not strips of metal placed in wells G1–G6?

_____

_____

_____

2. Why were strips of metal but no solutions added to wells A7–F7?

_____

_____

_____

3. Why did you clean the metal strips with the paper towel?

_____

_____

4. Using the number of reactions for each metal in Table 1, rank the metals from the most active to the least active.

_____

_____

_____

5. Solutions of dissolved metal compounds contain metal ions. An ion is an atom that has gained or lost electrons. Ions of metals are positively charged because the metals lose electrons when they react. The activity of the ion of a metal is a measure of how easily an ion gains electrons. Use the results of this experiment to rank the activities of ions of metals in solutions.

_____

_____

_____

6. How does the activity of an ion of a metal compare with the activity of the metal?

_____

_____

Strategy Check

_____ Can you identify evidence that a chemical reaction has occurred between a metal and a solution containing metal ions?

_____ Can you interpret evidence of chemical reactions between metals and solutions of metal ions and arrange the metals in order according to their activities?

LAB 1 Laboratory Activity

Chemical Reactions

The changes that occur during a chemical reaction are represented by a chemical equation. An equation uses chemical symbols to represent the substances that change. The reactants, on the left side of the equation, are the substances that react. The products, on the right side of the equation, are the substances that are formed from the reaction.

In the following reaction, two reactants form one product. Water and oxygen are the reactants. The product is hydrogen peroxide.

$$H_2O + \frac{1}{2}O_2 \rightarrow H_2O_2$$

A chemical reaction may have two products from the breakdown of a single reactant. In this example water is the reactant. Hydrogen and oxygen are products.

$$2H_2O \rightarrow 2H_2 + O_2$$

Two reactants can also combine to make two products. In the following reaction, carbon displaces the hydrogen in water and hydrogen and carbon monoxide are released as gases.

$$H_2O + C \rightarrow H_2 + CO$$

Strategy

You will recognize the reactants and products of a chemical reaction.
You will write a word equation for a chemical reaction.
You will write a balanced chemical equation using chemical symbols.

Materials

Part A	Part B	Part C
aluminum foil	matches	common nail, Fe
burner	test tube	steel wool
matches	spoon	string
tongs	baking soda, $NaHCO_3$	beaker
steel wool	test-tube holder	copper (II) sulfate solution, $CuSO_4$
	wood splint	watch or clock
		paper towel

WARNING: *Copper (II) sulfate solution is poisonous. Handle with care. Wear goggles and an apron.*

Procedure

Part A—Two Reactants→One Product

1. Observe the color of the steel wool. Record your observations in the Data and Observations section.

2. Predict changes in the steel wool when it is heated in the flame. Write your prediction in the Data and Observations section.

3. Protect the table with a sheet of aluminum foil. Place the burner in the center of the foil. Light the burner. **WARNING:** *Stay clear of flames.*

Figure 1

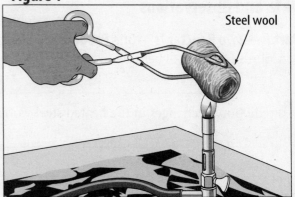

Steel wool

Laboratory Activity 1 (continued)

4. Hold the steel wool (containing iron, Fe) with the tongs over the flame as shown in Figure 1. As the steel wool burns, record the changes it goes through.

Part B—One Reactant→Two Products

1. Use the burner set up in Part A.
2. Place a spoonful of baking soda, $NaHCO_3$, in a test tube. Use the test-tube holder to heat the test tube in the flame, as shown in Figure 2. Do not point the mouth of the test tube toward anyone. In the Data and Observations section, write your prediction of what will happen as the baking soda is heated.
3. Record the description and colors of the products formed inside the tube as it is heated.
4. Test for the presence of CO_2. Light a wooden splint. Insert the flaming splint into the mouth of the test tube. If the flame of the splint goes out, CO_2 is present. Record your observations of the products of this reaction.

Part C—Two Reactants→Two Products

1. Carefully rub the nail with a piece of steel wool until the nail is shiny. Tie a string around the nail. Fill a beaker about half full with the $CuSO_4$ solution. Record the colors of the nail and the $CuSO_4$ solution in Table 1.

   WARNING: *Use care when handling sharp objects. Wash hands immediately after coming in contact with copper(II) sulfate solution.*

2. Dip the nail in the $CuSO_4$ solution. (See Figure 3.) Predict what changes will happen to the appearance of the nail and the solution. After 5 min, pull the nail from the solution and place it on a paper towel. Record the colors of the nail and the solution in Table 1.
3. Put the nail back into the solution and observe further color changes.

Figure 2

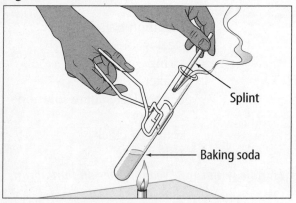

Splint

Baking soda

Figure 3

Data and Observations

Part A—Two Reactants→One Product

1. Color of steel wool before burning:

   _____

2. Prediction of changes in the heated steel wool:

   _____

   _____

Laboratory Activity 1 (continued)

3. Color of burned steel wool:

_____

Part B—One Reactant→Two Products

4. Prediction of changes in the heated baking soda:

_____

5. Description of deposits inside heated test tube:

_____

6. Observations of flaming splint:

_____

Part C—Two Reactants→Two Products

7. Prediction of changes in nail and $CuSO_4$ solution:

_____

Table 1

Observation time	Color of nail	Color of $CuSO_4$ solution
Before reaction	**8.**	**9.**
After reaction	**10.**	**11.**

Questions and Conclusions

1. Identify the two reactants in the heating of steel wool.

_____

_____

2. How does the heat from the flame affect the reactants when steel wool is heated?

_____

_____

3. What evidence suggests that at least two reactants were formed when $NaHCO_3$ was heated?

_____

_____

4. Was the heating of $NaHCO_3$ an endothermic or exothermic reaction? Explain your answer.

_____

_____

Laboratory Activity 1 (continued)

5. From your observations, does the reaction of an iron nail with the copper(II) sulfate yield more than one product?

_____

_____

_____

_____

6. Was the addition of the iron nail to the copper(II) sulfate solution an endothermic or exothermic reaction?

_____

Strategy Check

_____ Can you identify the reactants and products of a chemical reaction?

_____ Can you write a word equation for a chemical reaction?

_____ Can you write a balanced chemical equation using chemical symbols?

Reaction Rates and Temperature

Not all chemical reactions occur at the same rate. Some chemical reactions are very fast; others are very slow. The same chemical reaction can happen at several different rates depending on the temperature at which the reaction occurs

In this experiment, you will investigate the effect of temperature on a decomposition reaction. Household bleach is a solution of five percent sodium hypochlorite (NaClO). This compound decomposes to produce sodium chloride and oxygen gas.

$$2NaClO \rightarrow 2NaCl + O_2$$

Strategy

You will observe the amount of oxygen produced from the decomposition of household bleach at various temperatures.

You will graph the reaction data.

You will determine the relationship between reaction rate and temperature for this reaction.

Materials

beaker (400-mL)
thermometer
pipette, plastic microtip
2.5 percent NaClO solution
microplate (24-well)

Co(NO$_3$)$_2$ solution
pipette, plastic
washers, iron or lead (3 or 4)
clock with second hand
immersion heater or hot plate

WARNING: *Handle both solutions with care. Solutions can harm clothes and skin. Rinse spills with plenty of water.*

Procedure

Part A—Reaction at Room Temperature

1. Safety goggles and a laboratory apron must be worn throughout this experiment. Look at the equation of the decomposition reaction. In the Data and Observations section, write a prediction of what you might observe during this reaction. Write a hypothesis describing how temperature will affect this reaction rate.

2. Allow 400 mL of tap water to come to room temperature.

3. At the top of Table 1, measure and record the temperature of the water to the nearest 0.5°C.

4. Using the microtip pipette, place 30 drops of 2.5 percent sodium hypochlorite solution in well A1 of the microplate.

5. Rinse the microtip pipette twice with distilled water. Discard the rinse water.

6. Using the rinsed pipette, place 10 drops of cobalt nitrate solution into well C1 of the microplate.

7. Rinse the microtip pipette twice with distilled water. Discard the rinse water.

8. Draw up the sodium hypochlorite solution in well A1 into the bulb of the plastic pipette. Be sure that no solution remains in the stem of the pipette.

9. Place three or four iron or lead washers over the top of the stem of the pipette, as in Figure 1.

10. Turn the pipette upside down and squeeze and hold the pipette to expel the air from the bulb of the pipette.

11. While squeezing the pipette, bend the stem of the pipette over into the cobalt nitrate solution in well C1, as shown in Figure 2. Be prepared to start timing the reaction as soon as you complete the next two steps.

12. Release the pipette bulb and draw the cobalt nitrate solution into the pipette. The two solutions will mix. Record any changes you observe.

Laboratory Activity 2 (continued)

Figure 1

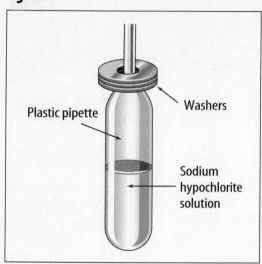

Plastic pipette

Washers

Sodium hypochlorite solution

13. While holding the pipette in place, quickly submerge the pipette bulb and washer assembly into the beaker of water as shown in Figure 3. Begin timing. If necessary, hold the pipette upright.
14. Count the number of bubbles produced by the reaction as they escape from the stem of the pipette every 15 s for 3 min. rRcord in Table 1 the total number of bubbles counted for each 15s interval.
15. Use Figure 4 to graph the data from Part A. Plot time on the X axis and the total number of bubbles on the Y-axis. Draw a line that best fits the data points.

Figure 3

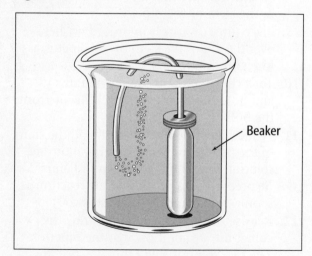

Beaker

Figure 2

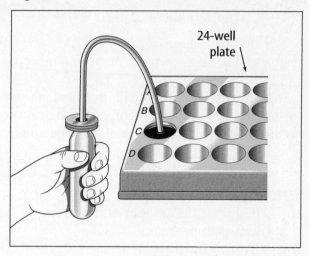

24-well plate

Part B—Reaction at a Higher Temperature
1. Place the beaker of water in the immersion bath or on the hot plate. Heat the water until its Celsius temperature is 10° higher than that of the room temperature water.
2. Repeat steps 3–14 in Part A, using the water bath at this higher temperature.
3. Plot your data from Part B on the same graph as Part A, but use a different colored pen or pencil.

Part C—Reaction at a Lower Temperature
1. Fill the beaker with tap water. Add ice to lower the Celsius temperature of the water 10° below that of the room temperature water.
2. Repeat steps 3–14 in Part A, using the water bath at this lower temperature.
3. Plot your data from Part C on the same graph as Part A, but use a third color.

Laboratory Activity 2 (continued)

Data and Observations

1. Prediction of reaction:

_____

2. Hypothesis relating reaction rate and temperature:

_____

Table 1

Time (s)	A. Total number of bubbles (room temperature) _____ °C	B. Total number of bubbles (higher temperature) _____ °C	C. Total number of bubbles (lower temperature) _____ °C
0			
15			
30			
45			
60			
75			
90			
105			
120			
135			
150			
165			
180			

Laboratory Activity 2 (continued)

Figure 4

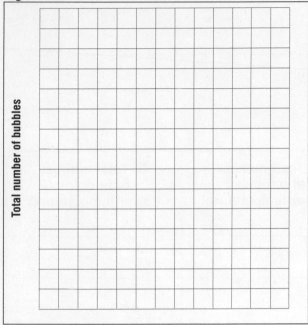

Total number of bubbles

Questions and Conclusions

1. How does raising the temperature affect the shape of the graphs that you plotted in Figure 4?

_____

2. Describe the relationship between reaction rate and temperature for the decomposition of
sodium hypochlorite._____

_____

_____

3. Why is it important that there be no sodium hypochlorite solution in the stem of the pipette in
step 8 of the procedure?_____

_____

4. Soft drinks contain carbonic acid (H_2CO_3). Carbonic acid decomposes to form water and carbon
dioxide as shown below $H_2CO_3 \rightarrow H_2O + CO_2$. Two soft drink bottles are opened, and one is placed
in a refrigerator while the other is left at room temperature. The carbonic acid in both bottles
decomposes, but one bottle goes "flat" faster than the other. Which bottle will go flat first? Explain.

_____

_____

Strategy Check

_____ Can you collect data on the amount of oxygen produced by the
decomposition of household bleach?

_____ Can you determine from a graph of the data how the reaction rate differs when
the temperature is changed?

Pushing People Around

When we push something, we unconsciously compensate for how much it weighs. We know that if an object is heavy it will require more force to get it moving and if it is light it will require less force. But how much difference is there? In this experiment, we will see what variables affect acceleration.

Strategy

You will see what happens when you use a constant force to pull a skater.
You will examine the relationship between force, acceleration, and mass.

Materials

tape
meterstick
roller skates
skating safety equipment (helmet, pads)
spring balance
stopwatch

Procedure

1. Mark positions on the floor at intervals of 0 m, 5 m, 10 m, and 15 m with the tape. The floor should be smooth, straight, and level.

2. Have one student stand on the 0-m mark with the skates on. A second student stands behind the mark and holds the skater. The skater holds the spring balance by its hook.

3. The third student holds the other end of the spring balance and exerts a constant pulling force on the skater. When the skater is released, the puller must maintain a constant force throughout the distance.

Measure the time to reach each of the marks. Record this in Table 1 in the Data and Observations section along with the spring balance readings at each mark.

4. Repeat steps 2 and 3 with skaters who have different masses. Keep the force the same. Make sure the skaters hold their skates parallel and do not try to change direction during the trial.

5. Repeat steps 2, 3, and 4 with a different constant force. Use the same three skaters. Record these results in Table 2 in the Data and Observations section.

Laboratory Activity 1 (continued)

Data and Observations

Table 1

Roller Skater Distance, Trial 1			
Trial	Distance (m)	Force (N)	Time (s)
1	5		
	10		
	15		
2	5		
	10		
	15		
3	5		
	10		
	15		

Table 2

Roller Skater Distance, Trial 2			
Trial	Distance (m)	Force (N)	Time (s)
1	5		
	10		
	15		
2	5		
	10		
	15		
3	5		
	10		
	15		

Laboratory Activity 1 (continued)

Questions and Conclusions

1. Until the time of Galileo and Newton, people believed that a constant force was required to produce a constant speed. Do your observations confirm or reject this notion?

_____

_____

2. What happens to the speed as you proceed farther along the measured distance?

_____

_____

3. What happens to the rate of increase in speed—the acceleration—as you proceed farther along the measured distance?

_____

_____

4. When the force is the same, how does the acceleration depend upon the mass?

_____

_____

5. When the mass of the skater is the same, how does the acceleration depend upon the force?

_____

_____

6. Suppose a 4 N force is applied to the skater and no movement results. How can this be explained?

_____

_____

_____

Strategy Check

_____ Can you pull someone with a constant force?

_____ Can you explain the relationship between force, mass, and acceleration?

Motion of a Bowling Ball

It takes time to walk somewhere. Sometimes you move quickly, while other times you move slowly. Other objects might show variation in their movement as well. In this lab, you will graph the movement of a bowling ball and consider how its motion relates to other kinds of motion.

Strategy

You will make a distance versus time graph of a bowling ball as it rolls. You will relate the motion of the bowling ball to other types of motion.

Materials

bowling ball
stopwatches (5–10)
large pillow

Procedure

1. Line up with other students at equally spaced distances of 1 m.
2. At the far end of the hall, set up the pillow or other large, soft object. This will prevent the ball from rolling too far.
3. Start your stopwatch when the ball is rolled slowly.
4. When the ball passes you, stop your stopwatch. As the ball passes the other students, they will do the same.
5. Record all of your times in Table 1.
6. Clear your stopwatch to prepare for another trial. This time, roll the ball faster.
7. Record your times in Table 2.
8. Graph the data for both tables, putting the data from Table 1 into Graph 1, and the data from Table 2 into Graph 2. Place the distance on the vertical axis, and the time on the horizontal axis.

Laboratory Activity 2 (continued)

Data and Observations

Table 1

Trial 1	
Distance	**Time**
0 m	
1 m	
2 m	
3 m	
4 m	
5 m	

Graph 1

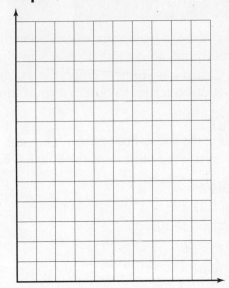

Table 2

Trial 2	
Distance	**Time**
0 m	
1 m	
2 m	
3 m	
4 m	
5 m	

Graph 2

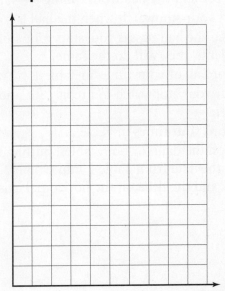

Questions and Conclusions

1. What do you notice about the graphs of the two trials?

_____

_____

2. On a distance versus time graph, what does the slope of the line tell you?

_____

_____

Laboratory Activity 2 (continued)

3. On a distance versus time graph, what does a flat (horizontal) line mean?

_____

_____

4. Imagine a bowling ball dropped from a great height. How would the motion of this bowling ball compare to the bowling balls in the lab?

_____

_____

_____

5. What was the speed of the bowling ball in the first trial? In the second trial?

_____

_____

6. What distance did the bowling balls travel? What is their displacement?

_____

7. How are distance and displacement related?

_____

_____

Strategy Check

_____ Can you graph the speed of an object in motion?

Static and Sliding Friction

When two objects are in contact, the molecules on one surface can attract molecules on the other surface. These surfaces are not smooth; small bumps and grooves exist. When one object slides over the other, the surfaces catch and stick as these bumps and grooves nestle together. The force that results between the surfaces is called friction. Many factors affect the force of friction, including the materials the surfaces are made from, how smooth the surfaces are, and how hard the surfaces are pressed together. For a block sliding on a level horizontal surface, the weight of the block pushes the bottom surface of the block against the horizontal surface.

When an object is at rest, static friction must be overcome to move the object. When one object is already sliding over another, sliding friction occurs. To keep the object moving, a force must be applied that is equal to the sliding friction force.

Strategy

You will calculate coefficients of static and sliding friction.
You will compare static friction to sliding friction.
You will describe the effect of weight on the force of friction.
You will determine the effect of surface area on friction.

Materials

eye hook   spring scale calibrated in newtons
set of masses   wood block (about 5 cm × 10 cm × 26 cm)

Procedure

1. Screw the eye hook into the end of the block. Weigh the wood block and eye hook using the spring scale. Record the weight in the table.

2. Lay the wood block on a flat surface as shown in Figure 1.

3. Find the force required to move the block from rest. Pull on the spring scale and notice the highest reading that occurs before the block moves. That is the static friction force.

Figure 1

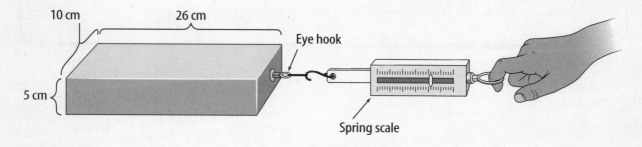

Laboratory Activity 1 (continued)

4. Find the force required to keep the block moving at a constant speed. As you pull on the spring scale, the reading will not be exact because the friction value will vary. Make the best judgment you can for the value of sliding friction. Record this value in the table.

5. Repeat steps 3 and 4 with different weights added on top of the friction block. Be sure to record the new weight of the block and its added weight.

6. Repeat steps 3 and 4 without masses added and with the block resting on a side with a different area.

7. Calculate the coefficient of static friction for each of the trials using the following equation.

$$\mu_{static} = \frac{static\ friction\ force}{weight}$$

8. Calculate the coefficient of sliding friction for each of the trials using the equation below.

$$\mu_{sliding} = \frac{sliding\ friction\ force}{weight}$$

9. Graph the relationship between the weight of the block and the force of static friction in Graph 1. Also graph the relationship between the force of sliding friction and the weight of the block in Graph 1.

Data and Observations

Table 1

Force of static friction	Force of sliding friction	Weight of block	μ_{Static}	$\mu_{Sliding}$	Area of side

Laboratory Activity 1 (continued)

Graph 1

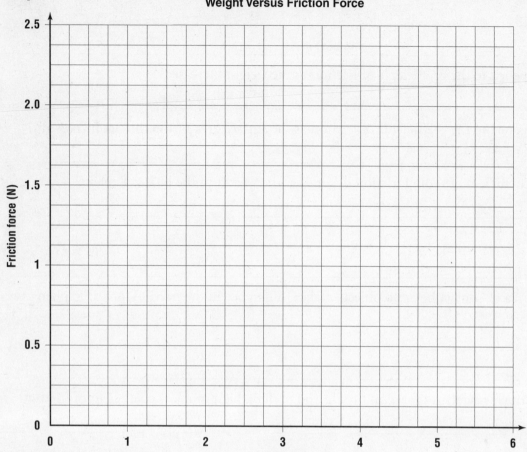

Weight Versus Friction Force

(y-axis: Friction force (N), marked at 0, 0.5, 1, 1.5, 2.0, 2.5)
(x-axis: Weight (N), marked at 0, 1, 2, 3, 4, 5, 6)

Questions and Conclusions

1. How did the addition of more weight affect the friction?

_____

2. How did the change in surface area of the contact between the block and the table affect the friction?

_____

3. How did the force of friction depend on the weight of the block?

_____

_____

4. Compare the size of static friction and sliding friction.

_____

_____

Laboratory Activity 1 (continued)

5. What could be a source of error in this experiment?

_____

_____

6. What happened to the coefficients of friction as the weight increased?

_____

7. What happened to the coefficients of friction as the surface area of the contact increased?

_____

8. Does the coefficient of sliding friction depend on the weight of the block? Explain.

_____

_____

_____

9. Does the area of contact between objects make a difference in the friction forces? Explain how you know.

_____

_____

10. If you are buying new tires for a car, would you prefer a high or a low coefficient of friction?

_____

_____

_____

Strategy Check

_____ Can you calculate coefficients of static and sliding friction?

_____ Do you understand the effects of weight and surface area on the force of friction?

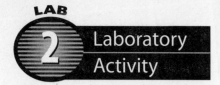

Newton's Second Law

Newton's second law of motion deals with acceleration, which is how quickly something speeds up or slows down. Acceleration depends on the mass of an object and the force pulling or pushing it. One way to write Newton's second law is *force = mass × acceleration.* Another way to think of Newton's second law is that if the same force acts on two objects, the object with the greater mass will accelerate more slowly.

Strategy
You will time the acceleration of a small toy car.
You will observe the effects of increasing mass on acceleration.

Materials
balance	modeling clay (about 300 g)	string or thread
large table	small toy car with free-spinning wheels	tape
meterstick	stopwatch	

Procedure
1. Cut a piece of string or thread 110 cm long. Tie a small loop in one end of the string.
2. Make a small ball of clay with a mass of about 2.5 g. Attach this ball of clay to the string by folding the clay around the loop. The loop will prevent the clay ball from falling off the string.
3. Divide the remaining clay into 40-g pieces.
4. Use your balance to measure the mass of the toy car. Write the mass of the car in the Data and Observations section.

Figure 1

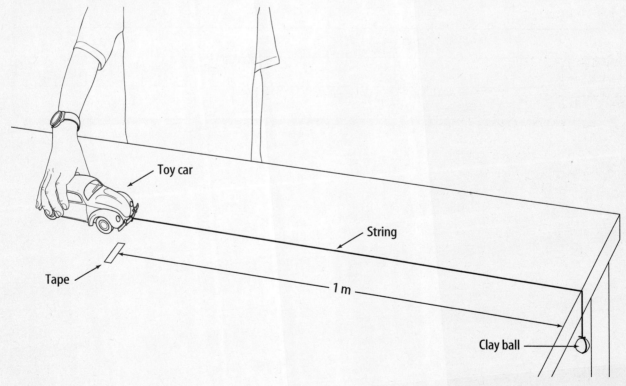

Laboratory Activity 2 (continued)

5. Use a meterstick to find a spot on the table 1 m from the edge. Mark it with a small piece of tape. This spot will be the starting point for the toy car during the experiment.

6. Put the front of the toy car at the starting point. Hold the piece of string on the table so that the clay ball is about 3 cm over the edge. Tape the other end of the string to the front of the toy car. Trim any excess string so that it does not interfere with the car's wheels. Check that your setup is similar to that shown in Figure 1.

7. Pick someone in your group to be the timer, someone to be the recorder, someone to hold the toy car in place and release it, and someone to catch it as it falls off the table.

8. Release the car. Use a stopwatch to measure the time it takes for the car to reach the table edge.

9. Write the travel time in Table 1.

10. Repeat steps 8 and 9 two more times. Use the data to calculate the average travel time for the car.

11. Add one 40-g piece of clay to the top of the car. Be careful that the clay does not interfere with the car's ability to roll freely.

12. Time three trips of the car. Record the travel times, calculate the average time, and record the average time in Table 1.

13. Repeat steps 11 and 12 until you have timed the car carrying 160 g of clay.

Data and Observations

Mass of car = _____ g

Table 1

Mass (g)		Travel Time (s)			
Total clay on top of car	Total car and clay	Time 1 (T1)	Time 2 (T2)	Time 3 (T3)	Average time (T1 + T2 + T3) / 3
0					
40					
80					
120					
160					

Laboratory Activity 2 (continued)

Graph 1

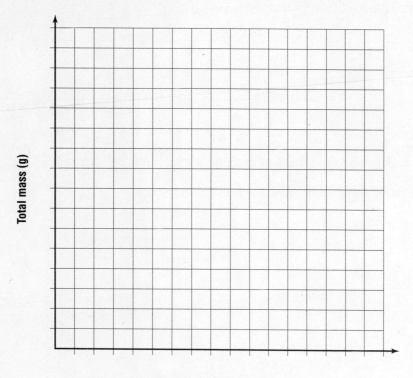

Average travel time (s)

Questions and Conclusions

1. Make a graph of total mass versus time in Graph 1.

2. Explain how your data support Newton's second law of motion.

_____

_____

_____

3. Why is it important to average three travel times for each one of the total masses?

_____

_____

4. What were some possible sources of error in this lab? In other words, what things might have caused differences in travel time for the same mass?

_____

_____

_____

_____

Laboratory Activity 2 (continued)

5. Use your graph to predict how much mass would be necessary to cause travel time of 15 s. Test your prediction. What happened?

_____

_____

_____

Strategy Check

_____ Do you understand the effects of increasing mass in acceleration?

_____ Can you relate force, mass, and acceleration?

Calculating Work and Power

LAB 1 Laboratory Activity

Chapter 20

When work is done on an object, energy is transferred to the object. When a force acts on an object and moves that object a certain distance, work is done on the object. Work (*W*) is defined by the following equation.

$$W = F \times d$$

In this equation, *F* represents a force acting on the object and *d* represents the distance through which the object moves as that force acts on it. In the metric system, force is measured in newtons (N), and distance is measured in meters (m). If a force of 1 newton acts on an object and the object moves 1 meter while the force is acting on it, the value of $F \times d$ equals 1 newton-meter (N-m), which is the same as to 1 joule (J) of energy being transferred.

Power (*P*) is the rate at which work is done. It can be calculated by the following equation.

$$P = W/t$$

In this equation, *W* represents the work done and *t* represents the amount of time required to do the work. In the metric system, the unit of power is the watt (W). If 1 joule of work is done in 1 second, W/t has a value of 1 J/s, which is equal to 1 watt.

Strategy

You will determine the amount of work required to lift an object.
You will determine the power used while lifting the object.

Materials

spring scale   string   wire tie (plastic-coated)
mass (1-kg)   dowel (wood, about 50 cm long)   meterstick
scissors   masking tape   stopwatch

Procedure

Figure 1

1. Weigh the 1-kg mass using the metric spring scale. Record this value in the Data and Observations section.
2. Cut a 1.3-m length of string. Tightly tie one end of the string to the center of the wood dowel. Secure the knot with a piece of masking tape to prevent the string from slipping.
3. Make a small loop at the other end of the string and knot it. Attach the 1-kg mass to the loop with a plastic-coated wire tie.
4. Measure a 1-m distance along the string from the dowel using the meterstick. Mark this distance on the string with a small strip of masking tape.
5. Hold the dowel at both ends as shown in Figure 1.

Laboratory Activity 1 (continued)

6. Raise the 1-kg mass by winding up the string on the dowel as shown in Figure 2. Keep the winding motion steady so that the string winds up and the mass rises at a constant speed. Practice raising the mass in this manner several times.

7. You are now ready to have your lab partner measure the time it takes for you to raise the mass a distance of 1 m.

8. Suspend the 1-kg mass from the dowel as before. At a signal from your lab partner, begin to raise the mass at a constant speed by winding the string on the dowel.

Figure 2

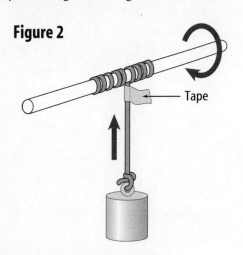

Tape

Have your lab partner use a stopwatch to measure the time required for the piece of masking tape on the string to reach the dowel. Record this value under Student 1 in Table 1.

9. Reverse roles with your lab partner and allow him or her to repeat steps 6–8. Record the time value under Student 2 in Table 1.

10. The size of the force that was needed to raise the 1-kg mass is equal to the weight of 1 kg. The distance that the 1-kg mass was raised is the distance between the dowel and the piece of masking tape, which is 1 m. Record the values for the force and distance under Student 1 and Student 2 in Table 1.

11. Calculate the work you did to raise the 1-kg mass and record this value under Student 1 in Table 2.

12. Calculate the power you developed lifting the 1-kg mass. Record the value under Student 1 in Table 2.

13. Complete Table 2 using your lab partner's data from Table 1.

Data and Observations

Weight of 1-kg mass: _____

Table 1

Measurement	Student 1	Student 2
time		
force (N)		
distance		

Laboratory Activity 1 (continued)

Table 2

Calculation	Student 1	Student 2
work (J)		
power (W)		

Questions and Conclusions

1. Compare the amounts of work that you and your lab partner did.

   _____

   _____

2. Why would you expect both amounts of work to be the same?

   _____

   _____

3. Compare the amounts of power developed by you and your lab partner.

   _____

   _____

4. Why would you expect the amounts of power to differ?

   _____

   _____

5. How do the amounts of work and power depend on the speed at which the 1-kg mass is lifted?

   _____

   _____

   _____

Strategy Check

_____ Can you determine the amount of work required to lift an object?

_____ Can you determine the power used while lifting an object?

LAB 2 Laboratory Activity

The Bicycle

You have learned about many simple machines that are used in compound machines. The bicycle is a familiar compound machine that uses a wheel and axle.

James Starley designed and manufactured one of the first successful bicycles in 1868. He developed his design so that once it was moving, only a small amount of force would be required to keep the vehicle and driver in motion on level ground.

A multigear bicycle can either multiply its speed or increase the force on the wheels. However, it can never do both at the same time. If the bicycle's gears increase the force on the wheels, then the pedals turn at a faster rate than the wheels do. If the gears decrease the force on the wheels, the wheels turn faster than the pedals. The mechanical advantage of a bicycle is the number of times the force applied by the rider's legs is multiplied. The speed advantage is the number of times the wheel turns for each rotation of the pedals. As the mechanical advantage increases, the speed advantage decreases.

Strategy

You will determine the mechanical advantage and the speed advantage of a multigear bicycle.
You will explain the relationship between mechanical advantage and speed advantage.
You will describe the distance traveled by a bicycle depending on the gear combination used.

Materials 🧤 🥽 🔧

30-cm-long block of wood
multigear bicycle
meterstick

Procedure

1. Place a block of wood under the bottom bracket of the bicycle's frame so the rear wheel is lifted off the ground. Have your lab partner steady the bicycle by holding the handle bars and the seat as shown in Figure 1.

2. **WARNING:** *Avoid placing your hand or any object near the rear wheel, chain, or gears.* Rotate the pedals with one of your hands to make the rear wheel turn. Shift the gears and observe the speed of the rear wheel as you shift through each gear. Be sure to continue rotating the pedal as you switch gears. Switching gears without moving the pedal may result in the chain jumping off the gears. Record your observations in the Data and Observations section.

3. Remove the bicycle from the block of wood and lay it on its side. Count the number of teeth in each gear of both the front section and rear section. Record the data in Table 1.

Figure 1

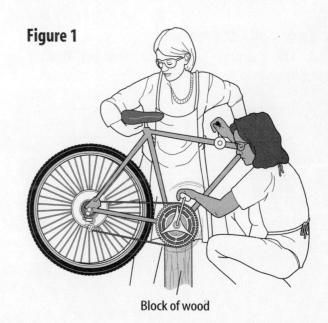

Block of wood

Laboratory Activity 2 (continued)

Figure 2

Rear gears   Front gears

4. Measure the diameter of the bicycle's rear wheel to the nearest centimeter. Record this in the Data and Observations section.

5. Set the bicycle upright. Place the gears in the lowest gear combination, with the chain on the smallest sprocket of the front gears and the largest sprocket of the back gears.

6. Measure how many centimeters the bicycle travels as the pedal makes one complete revolution. Mark the starting and ending points using the front edge of the front tire and measure the distance between these two points. Record this distance in the Experimental column in the data table.

7. Repeat steps 5 and 6 for each of the other gear combinations. Record your observations.

Data and Observations

1. Effect shifting gears has on the rear wheel speed:

_____

_____

2. Bicycle's rear wheel diameter:

_____

8. Calculate the mechanical advantage (M.A.) for each gear combination using the equation below. Record your answers.

$$M.A. = \frac{\text{number of teeth on rear gear}}{\text{number of teeth on front gear}}$$

9. Calculate the speed advantage (S.A.) for each gear combination using the equation below. Record your answers.

$$S.A. = \frac{\text{number of teeth on front gear}}{\text{number of teeth on rear gear}}$$

10. Find the theoretical distance the bicycle should travel as the pedal makes one revolution for each gear combination using the equation below. Record your answers. ($\pi = 3.14$)

Distance = S.A. × rear wheel diameter × π

11. Calculate the experimental error between the theoretical and the experimental distance traveled using the equation below. Record your answers.

Percent error =

$$\frac{\text{theoretical} - \text{experimental}}{\text{theoretical}} \times 100\%$$

12. Graph the mechanical advantage versus the speed advantage on graph 1.

Graph 1

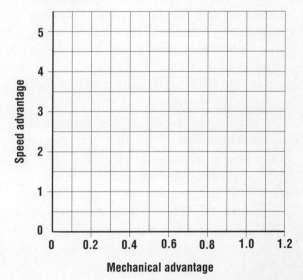

Laboratory Activity 2 (continued)

Table 1

Front teeth	Rear teeth	M.A.	S.A.	Experimental distance (cm)	Theoretical distance (cm)	Percent error

Questions and Conclusions

1. Why is a high mechanical advantage important to bicycle riders?

_____

_____

2. Why is a high speed advantage important to bicycle riders?

_____

_____

3. What simple machines are involved in a bicycle?

_____

_____

4. What is the mathematical relationship between mechanical advantage and speed advantage?

_____

_____

_____

Laboratory Activity 2 (continued)

5. Which gear combination produced the greatest mechanical advantage in the bicycle you tested?

_____

6. Which gear combination produced the greatest speed advantage in the bicycle you tested?

_____

_____

_____

7. Under what conditions is friction useful in riding a bicycle?

_____

_____

_____

8. How does friction make riding a bicycle more difficult?

_____

_____

_____

Strategy Check

_____ Can you determine the mechanical advantage and the speed advantage of a multigear bicycle?

_____ Can you explain the relationship between mechanical advantage and speed advantage?

_____ Can you describe the distance traveled by a bicycle depending on the gear combination used?

The Effect of Temperature on Diffusion and Expansion

Chapter 21

The temperature of a substance is related to the average kinetic energy of the molecules the substance is made from. The kinetic energy of a molecule or any object increases when it moves faster. Because temperature depends on the average kinetic energy of molecules, when the temperature of something increases, the kinetic energy of its molecules increases. As a result, its molecules move faster. Most materials expand as their temperature increases and their molecules move faster. Gases usually expand much more than solids or liquids as they become hotter.

When one liquid is added to another, the molecules of the two liquids will move through each other, or diffuse, at a rate that depends on the temperatures of the liquids. In this lab you will observe the effect of temperature on the diffusion of liquids and the expansion of a gas.

Strategy

You will observe the effect of temperature on the expansion of air.
You will observe the effect of temperature on the diffusion of two liquids.

Materials

250 mL beakers (3)
water
hot plate
crushed ice
food coloring (3 drops)

round balloons (3)
permanent marker
flexible tape measure
ice chest
hair dryer

Procedure

Part A—Diffusion in Water

1. In groups of three or four, set up your water temperature and diffusion activity. Pour water into two beakers until they are about two thirds full. Place one beaker on the hot plate, and begin to warm the water slowly to just under a boil. Let one beaker sit at room temperature. Fill the third beaker with crushed ice. Continue with step 2 of Part A when the water in the first beaker is almost boiling and the water in the third beaker is almost melted.

2. Check that the water in the beaker on the hot plate is near boiling. Look for tiny bubbles to appear on the surface of the glass. Do not let the water boil. Remove beaker from hot plate and turn off hot plate. Convection currents in boiling water would interfere with your results. **CAUTION:** *Use proper protection when handling the heated beaker.*

3. Have two students in the group gently move the cold and room-temperature beakers side by side. Try to disturb the water as little as possible. Have the water as still as possible before continuing. Gently let a drop of food coloring fall into the water in each beaker. Observe how the dye falls and spreads throughout the water. Do not stir or move the beakers during this time. Look how quickly the dye moves around the water. Does it sit on the bottom? In which beaker does the dye spread more quickly? Record your results in Table 1 in the Data and Observations section.

Laboratory Activity 1 (continued)

4. Now carefully let a drop of the dye slip into the beaker of hot water. Do not stir the water in any manner. How quickly does the dye spread throughout the water? How does the movement in the near boiling water compare to the movement of the dye in the room temperature and near freezing water? Record your observations in Table 1. What does this tell you about the speed of the molecules in each temperature of water?

Part B—Expansion in Air

1. Inflate three round balloons to about the same size. Blow them up so that they are almost full of air, but leave enough room for expansion. With your marker, label the balloons with your group name. Then, make a mark on each balloon at a vertical center where you will measure the circumference. Finally, label the balloons *Cold, Room,* and *Hot.*

2. Use a tape measure to measure the circumference of each balloon. Use the mark you made on the vertical center of each balloon as a guide to determine where to measure. Record the circumference of each balloon in Table 2 in the Data and Observations section.

3. Place your balloon labeled *Cold* in an ice chest that is about one-fourth full of ice. Close the lid and wait five minutes.

4. Meanwhile, use the hair dryer to gently sweep hot air back and forth across the surface of the balloon labeled *Hot.* Do not overheat. Keep the dryer at least six inches from the balloon's surface. Heat for about three minutes. Immediately measure the circumference of the balloon again at the vertical center mark. Be as quick as possible so the air in the balloon does not cool down. Record this value in Table 2.

5. Take the balloon from the ice chest and measure its circumference at the vertical center mark. Record the measurement in Table 2.

6. Finally, measure the circumference of your balloon labeled *Room.* Record the value in Table 2.

7. Calculate the changes in the circumference of each balloon. Record the values in Table 2. Remember to include plus or minus signs to show whether your balloon expanded or contracted.

Laboratory Activity 1 (continued)

Data and Observations

Table 1

Water temperature	Description of how dye moved through water
Room	1.
Cold	2.
Hot	3.

Table 2

Temperature of air in balloon	Circumference (cm)		
	Beginning	End	Change (±)
Room			
Cold			
Hot			

Questions and Conclusions

1. What happened to the circumference of the cold balloon? Explain why this happened.

   _____

   _____

2. Did the hot balloon expand or contract? Why did the circumference of the hot balloon get larger?

   _____

   _____

Laboratory Activity 1 (continued)

3. Describe and explain the change in the circumference of the room temperature balloon.

_____

_____

4. Describe the change in the temperature of each balloon in terms of the motion of the air molecules.

_____

_____

5. In which beaker were the water molecules moving the fastest?

_____

_____

6. Explain how the rate at which the dye diffused in the different beakers is related to the temperature of the water.

_____

_____

Strategy Check

_____ Can you compare the thermal energy of air molecules at different temperatures?

_____ Can you observe the thermal energy of water molecules at different temperatures?

Observing Radiation

Have you ever walked barefoot on asphalt on a sunny summer day? The black pavement is hot because heat from the sun transfers to the pavement through radiation. Radiation is the movement of energy in the form of waves. Different materials absorb radiant energy from the sun differently. In today's experiment, you will compare how light-colored materials and dark-colored materials differ in their ability to absorb energy from the sun.

Strategy

You will observe how energy from the sun can increase the temperature of water.
You will determine how color influences how much solar radiation is absorbed.

Materials

construction paper (black)
construction paper (white)
containers (2 plastic, 500-mL)
scissors
tape
graduated cylinder (100-mL)
water
thermometer (alcohol, Celsius)
timer
pencils (colored)

Procedure

WARNING: *Use care when handling sharp objects.*

1. Fasten black construction paper on the bottom and sides of one container.
2. Fasten white construction paper on the bottom and sides of the other container.
3. Add 250 mL of room-temperature water to each container.
4. Use a thermometer to find the temperature of the water in each container. Record your data in Table 1 in the Data and Observations section.
5. Place the containers side by side in direct sunlight outside on a sunny windowsill. Be sure both containers receive the same amount of sunshine.
6. Measure the temperature of the water in each container at 5-minute intervals for 30 minutes. Record your data in Table 1.
7. Using Figure 2, graph the data from the table, using a line graph. Use one colored pencil to show data for the light container and a different one to show data for the dark container. Draw lines to connect the temperature for each container of water.

Figure 1

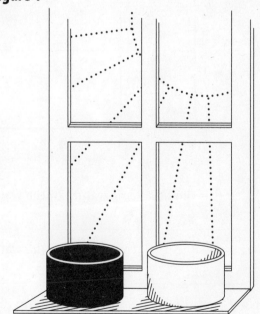

Laboratory Activity 2 (continued)

Data and Observations

Table 1

Color of container	Time (min)						
	0	5	10	15	20	25	30
Temp. (°C)—Light							
Temp. (°C)—Dark							

Figure 2

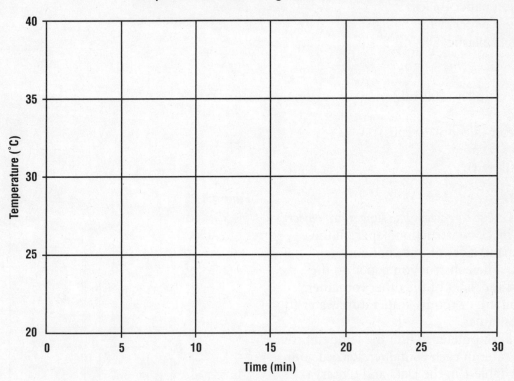

Temperature of Water in Light and Dark Containers

1. What was the final temperature of the water in the dark container?

_____

2. What was the final temperature of the water in the light container?

_____

3. How many degrees did the temperature of the dark container increase?

_____

4. How many degrees did the temperature of the light container increase?

_____

Laboratory Activity 2 (continued)

Questions and Conclusions

1. Did one container of water heat up more quickly? Which one?

_____

2. How do you think color influences the ability of an object to absorb energy from the sun?

_____

_____

_____

_____

3. Would you get similar results if you placed the containers in the shade? Why or why not?

_____

_____

4. If you were stranded in a hot desert, would you rather be wearing a dark-colored or a light-colored T-shirt? Why?

_____

_____

_____

_____

Strategy Check

_____ Did you observe the influence of solar radiation on water temperature?

_____ Did you determine how color influences the absorption of solar radiation?

Conductivity of Various Metals

Some materials are excellent conductors of electricity, while other materials do not conduct electricity at all. For example, metals are generally good conductors of electricity, whereas materials like wood and rubber do not conduct electricity. That is why electricians generally wear rubber gloves to protect their hands from electric shock. You will investigate how well various materials conduct electricity.

Strategy

You will determine how well different materials conduct electricity.
You will observe the behavior of a diode.

Materials

Testable Materials
aluminum foil
brass screw
copper pipe
diode
glass rod
graphite (pencil lead)
nail
paper clip
plastic pen cap
rubber eraser
wooden stick

Circuit Parts
alligator clips (2)
20-cm lengths of insulated copper wire (4)
lightbulbs (2)
lightbulb holders (2)
1.5-V batteries (2)
wire strippers

CAUTION: *Be careful working with sharp objects.*

Procedure

1. Set up a test circuit as shown in Figure 1 and described below.
2. With wire strippers, carefully scrape off 1 cm of insulation at the end of each wire.
3. Attach two wires to each of the lightbulb holders.
4. Attach one wire from each of the lightbulb holders to one exposed terminal of the batteries.
5. Leave the other wire from each lightbulb holder unattached. Attach an alligator clip to the free ends of the wires.
6. Put a lightbulb in each lightbulb holder.

Figure 1

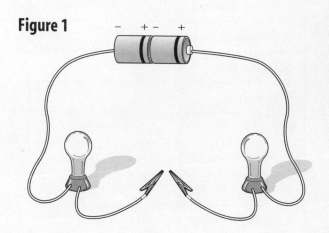

Laboratory Activity 1 (continued)

7. Before testing each material, predict whether it will allow the lightbulbs to light. Record your prediction in Table 1.
8. Test each material by attaching the alligator clips to each end as shown in Figure 2. Record your observations in Table 1
9. Reverse the direction of current in each material by switching the alligator clips. Record your observations in Table 1.
10. After testing all the materials, dismantle the circuit and place the components where instructed by your teacher.

Figure 2

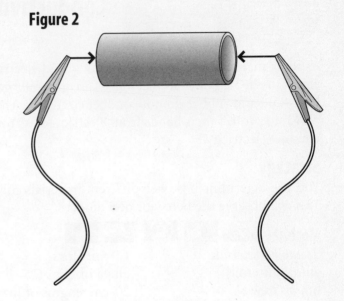

Data and Observations

Table 1

Material	Prediction before connecting	Observations when initially connected	Observations when connected in reverse
1. Aluminum foil			
2. Brass screw			
3. Copper pipe			
4. Glass rod			
5. Graphite			
6. Nail			
7. Paper clip			
8. Plastic pen cap			
9. Rubber eraser			
10. Wooden stick			
11. Diode			

Laboratory Activity 1 (continued)

Questions and Conclusions

1. From the data in Table 1, prepare a list of the materials that are conductors of electricity.

   _____

   _____

2. From the data in Table 1, prepare a list of materials that are not conductors.

   _____

   _____

3. Did any of the materials appear in both lists?

   _____

   _____

4. How can you tell when there is a current in the circuit?

   _____

   _____

   _____

5. Were all of the metal materials good conductors of electricity?

   _____

   _____

6. Of the materials that conducted electricity, were there any nonmetals?

   _____

7. Which materials would make good insulators?

   _____

   _____

8. How could a diode be used in a circuit?

   _____

   _____

Strategy Check

_____ Can you determine how well different materials conduct electricity?

_____ Can you observe the behavior of a diode?

Laboratory Activity 2 — Batteries

A wet-cell battery converts chemical energy into electrical energy. Chemical reactions taking place at each of the battery terminals cause electrons to pile up at the negative terminal. Voltage is a measure of the force that causes electrons to flow from the negative terminal to the positive terminal through a conductor. The flow of charges through a conductor is current.

The amounts of voltage and current produced by a battery depend on the nature and the concentration of the chemicals in the battery. For example, a car battery produces more current and voltage than a flashlight battery does. A car battery also contains chemicals that differ in nature and concentration from the chemicals in a flashlight battery.

Strategy
You will build wet-cell batteries.
You will measure the voltage of the batteries.

Materials
250-mL beaker
aluminum foil, heavy gauge
glass rod
alligator clips (2)
copper strip

wires (2)
voltmeter
100 mL graduated cylinder
0.1 M hydrochloric acid

water
paper towels
vinegar
aluminum strip

Procedure
1. Line the inside of a 250-mL beaker with aluminum foil. The foil should hang over the outside edges of the beaker as shown in Figure 1.
2. Place a glass rod across the mouth of the beaker.
3. Using an alligator clip, hang a copper strip from the glass rod into the beaker. The copper strip should hang near one side of the beaker, but the copper strip should NOT touch the aluminum foil.
4. Attach a wire to the alligator clip. Then attach the other end of the wire to the positive (+) terminal of the voltmeter.
5. Attach a second alligator clip to the aluminum foil hanging over the edge of the beaker. This second alligator clip should be attached across from the copper strip as shown in Figure 1.

Figure 1

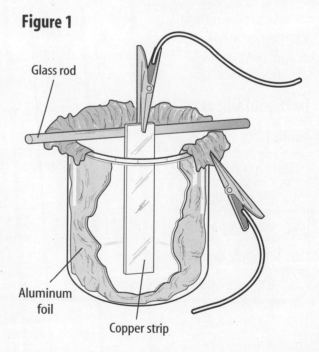

Glass rod

Aluminum foil

Copper strip

Laboratory Activity 2 (continued)

6. Attach a wire to the second alligator clip and connect the other end of this wire to the negative (–) terminal of the voltmeter as shown in Figure 2.

7. Observe the wet cell and record any changes in Table 1. Observe the voltage on the voltmeter and record it in Table 1.

8. Carefully add 75 mL of 0.1 M HCl to the foil-lined beaker. **CAUTION:** *HCl can cause burns. Rinse any acid spills immediately with water.*

9. After adding HCl, observe the wet cell and notice any changes to the system. Record your observations in Table 1.

10. Observe the voltage on the voltmeter and record the reading in Table 1.

11. Disconnect the wires. Under your teacher's supervision, carefully empty the acid from the beaker. Thoroughly rinse the beaker and copper strip with water and dry them with paper towels. Discard the aluminum foil.

12. Repeat steps 1 through 10 using vinegar instead of HCl. Be sure to always use new aluminum foil.

13. Repeat steps 1 through 10 using an aluminum strip instead of the copper strip. Be sure to use fresh hydrochloric acid and fresh aluminum foil.

Figure 2

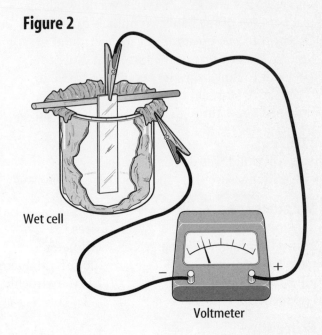

Wet cell

Voltmeter

Data and Observations

Table 1

Battery conditions	Changes to system	Voltage reading
1. Without liquid		
2. HCl, copper, aluminum		
3. Vinegar, copper, aluminum		
4. HCl, aluminum, aluminum		

Laboratory Activity 2 (continued)

Questions and Conclusions

1. From the data in Table 1, determine which battery conditions produced the largest voltage.

_____

_____

_____

2. Which liquid—HCl or vinegar—produced a higher voltage? Explain.

_____

_____

_____

3. How do you know that a chemical reaction took place in the battery after the vinegar was added?

_____

_____

_____

4. What metals were used to produce the batteries? How did they affect the results?

_____

_____

_____

5. How did the effect of hydrochloric acid on the copper strip differ from its effect on the aluminum foil?

_____

_____

_____

Strategy Check

_____ Can you build a wet-cell battery?

_____ Can you measure the voltages produced by different wet-cell batteries?

LAB 1 Laboratory Activity

Earth's Magnetism

Earth is surrounded by a magnetic field that is similar to the magnetic field around a bar magnet. Magnets have a north magnetic pole and a south magnetic pole. Earth's south magnetic pole is near the north geographic pole, and its north magnetic pole is near the south geographic pole.

You usually do not notice Earth's magnetic field because it is weak. In your classroom, wires carrying electric current also produce magnetic fields that add to Earth's magnetic field and can change its direction. A compass can show the direction of the magnetic field. A compass needle is a small bar magnet that aligns itself along the magnetic field lines around the compass. You can use a compass to map the magnetic field in your classroom.

Strategy

You will use a compass.
You will map the magnetic field in your classroom.

Materials

compass
graph paper

Procedure

1. Draw a floor plan of the classroom on the graph paper. (The floor plan does not have to be to scale.) Indicate north, south, east, and west on the floor plan.
2. Mark the desk locations on the floor plan with a small circle and a number.
3. Take a compass reading at each numbered location. Note the compass needle's direction. See Figure 1. Draw it neatly on the floor plan. Record each angle in Table 1.

Figure 1

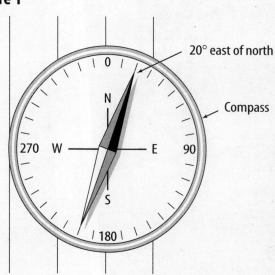

20° east of north

Compass

Data and Observations

Table 1

Location	Angle
1	
2	
3	
4	
5	
6	
7	

Laboratory Activity 1 (continued)

Questions and Conclusions

1. In what direction did your compass needle point in most of the readings?

_____

2. Where did the largest changes in the direction of the compass needle occur?

_____

_____

_____

3. What might have caused the direction of the compass needle to change in your classroom?

_____

_____

4. Draw a diagram of Earth showing the relative positions of the geographic axis and the magnetic axis.

Strategy Check

_____ Can you use a compass?

_____ Can you make a magnetic map of your classroom?

Magnetic Codes

Audiocassette tapes, videotapes, and computer diskettes are all forms of magnetically recorded information. An electromagnet records a series of magnetic codes on the tape or disk. When the tape or disk is read, an electromagnet converts these codes into electric currents that are used to produce words, sounds, and images.

Strategy

You will create a magnetically coded message on a strip of paper.
You will read a magnetic code on a strip of paper.

Materials

1 very small disk magnet, no more than 5 mm in diameter
    (can also be cut out of a flexible magnetic strip)
masking tape
paper or plastic cup, or film canister
paper
scissors
pencil
4 disk magnets
ruler

4-Digit Letter Codes			
A 0000	E 1111	R 0010	U 1011
B 1000	I 0100	S 0011	P 1001
C 1100	O 0110	N 0001	H 0101
D 1110	T 0111	L 1010	F 1101

Procedure

1. Mark one side of the tiny magnet with tape. This side represents "1" and the other side represents "0." Put it in the cup. This is your reader magnet.
2. Cut a piece of paper about 5 cm wide and 30 cm long.
3. Choose a letter from the list above to encode. Write the letter and your group's number on the back of the paper strip.
4. Tape a magnet to the back of the paper strip near one end.
5. Turn the paper over and mark that end of the paper "start." Put the reader magnet over the strip.

If the reader magnet shows the wrong number (your first number is 1 and it shows 0), untape the magnet from the back, flip it over, and retape it.

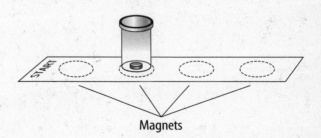

Magnets

Laboratory Activity 2 (continued)

6. Repeat step 5 with each of the other three magnets until you have four magnets taped in a line to the back of the paper. These four magnets should spell out the 4-digit code you selected.

7. Exchange codes with at least three groups. For each, use the reader magnet to read their code. Check your answer against the letter written on the back of the strip. Record your results.

Data and Observations

Your group _____ _____ _____ _____ letter _____

1st exchange _____ _____ _____ _____ letter _____

2nd exchange _____ _____ _____ _____ letter _____

3rd exchange _____ _____ _____ _____ letter _____

Questions and Conclusions

1. Did you successfully read the other groups' codes? Explain.

_____

_____

_____

2. How could you make certain that all the groups could read the other groups' codes?

_____

_____

_____

_____

Strategy Check

_____ Can you create a magnetically coded message on a strip of paper?

_____ Can you read a magnetic code on a strip of paper?

Transverse Waves

You are surrounded by a variety of waves such as visible light waves, sound waves, and radio waves. These waves interact with matter, and waves of the same type interact with each other. You are about to explore two questions. What happens when a wave strikes a boundary between two materials? What happens when two waves traveling in the same material meet?

Strategy

You will use a long rope to observe the behavior of a wave at a boundary. You will observe the behavior of waves that travel from both ends of a long rope and meet in the middle.

Materials

rope, 8–10 meters long

Procedure

1. Make a data table in your Science Journal like the one shown to record your observations. Be sure to leave enough room for your comments.
2. With a partner, lay the rope on the floor and stretch the rope to its full length. Hold one end of the rope still while your partner creates a wave with a single crest or trough by moving their end of the rope horizontally back and forth. Observe the behavior of the wave when it reaches the end of the rope and strikes a boundary—your hand.

3. Using the same procedure as before, create a single crest of a wave in both ends of the rope at the same time. Observe the behavior of the wave when the two crests meet in the center of the rope.
4. Using the same procedure, create a crest at one end of the rope and a trough at the other end of the rope at the same time. Observe the behavior of the wave when the crest and trough meet in the center of the rope.

Data and Observations

Wave Observations	
Wave	**Observation**
Step 2	
Step 3	
Step 4	

Laboratory Activity 1 (continued)

Questions and Conclusions

1. What changes occurred in the wave in step 2 when the wave hit the boundary?

   _____

   _____

2. Did the wave have the same amount of energy after it hit the boundary? Explain.

   _____

   _____

3. What happened when the waves met in the center of the rope in steps 3 and 4?

   _____

   _____

4. Infer why the size of the waves changed when the two waves met in steps 3 and 4.

   _____

   _____

5. Infer how you can determine the amplitude of the wave created when two waves traveling in opposite directions on the same rope meet.

   _____

   _____

Strategy Check

_____ Can you describe what happens when a wave strikes a boundary?

_____ Can you describe what happens when two waves traveling in opposite directions on the same rope meet?

Scattering of Light Waves

On a sunny day, you might have seen dust particles in a beam of sunlight. When light waves in the sunbeam strike a dust particle, they are reflected in all directions. This process, in which light traveling in one direction is made to travel in many directions, is called scattering. Sunlight is scattered when it strikes dust particles floating in the air. You see the dust particles as bright specks of light when some of these scattered light waves enter your eyes. Just like dust particles, tiny droplets of water in the air can cause scattering. Also, milk contains tiny particles of milk fat that can cause scattering of light waves.

Strategy

You will use a clear glass beaker, water, whole milk, and a flashlight to observe the scattering of light by particles of milk fat in a beaker of water.

You will record your observations in a data table as more milk is added to the water.

Materials

clear glass 500-mL beaker
50-mL beaker
whole milk
eye dropper
small flashlight
3" x 5" index card (2)
hole punch
distilled water

Procedure

1. Turn off the lights in the room and darken the room. Allow enough light into the room so that you can safely work.

2. Put about 250 mL of distilled water into the 500-mL beaker.

3. Put about 25 mL of whole milk into the 50-mL beaker. This will be used later in the lab.

4. Use a hole punch to make a hole in one of the index cards. Position the hole so that the center of the flashlight goes through the hole when the card is sitting on the lab table.

5. Place the index card with the hole next to the clear beaker of water. Have a lab partner hold the other index card about 30 cm away from the beaker directly opposite the index card with the hole.

6. Turn on the flashlight and hold it against the index card with the hole. Position the flashlight so that the center of the beam goes through the hole in the index card. Observe the image on the index card on the other side of the beaker.

7. Record your observations in your data table.

8. Add ½ dropper of milk to the water in the beaker and stir. Repeat steps 5–7.

9. Repeat step 8 until the water appears to look more like milk than water.

Laboratory Activity 2 (continued)

Data and Observations

Amount of Milk	Observations
No Milk	

Questions and Conclusions

1. What did you observe when the light traveled through the beaker that contained only water?

_____

_____

2. What did you observe when the light traveled through the beaker of water as you progressively added more milk?

_____

_____

3. Why did adding more milk to the beaker cause the image on the index card to change?

_____

_____

Strategy Check

_____ Can you describe how a light beam is affected when it travels through a medium that does not contain other particles?

_____ Can you describe how a light beam is affected as it travels through a medium that contains particles of another material?

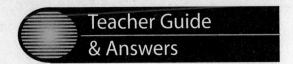

Chapter 1   The Nature of Science

Laboratory Activity 1 (page 1)

Lab Note: Prepare red cabbage juice by boiling the outer leaves in a small amount of water. Do not add salt or other seasonings. Pour off the juice. (The cabbage can then be eaten.) Red cabbage juice should be refrigerated if kept overnight as it will ferment. It can be kept in the refrigerator for two to three weeks. Flower petals can be used in place of red cabbage juice. Place a petal in each test tube. The petals will change color when treated with the chemicals.

Lab Note: Prepare the baking soda solution by dissolving 5 g baking soda in 95 mL distilled water.

Procedure

1. Answers will vary. Some students may say that color changes will occur.

Data and Observations

Table 1

Test tube 1; vinegar; red
Test tube 2; ammonia; purple
Test tube 3; baking soda solution; purple
Test tube 4; nothing; red

Questions and Conclusions

1. **a.** Answers will vary
   b. the hypothesis
2. no
3. These are the data based on observations. Data must be recorded in order to be compared and analyzed.
4. form a hypothesis, do an experiment, observe, analyze data, draw conclusions
5. It is used for comparing changes that occur in an experiment.
6. It is a proposed solution based on known facts.
7. Yes, the experiment showed (or did not show) if the hypothesis was correct.
8. Answers will vary.

Lab Note: Students can determine if the chemicals used are acids or bases by testing with litmus paper.

Laboratory Activity 2 (page3)

Lab Note: Purchase bouillon cubes in a grocery store. Dissolve in boiling water before class begins.

Lab Note: Instruct students to use the proper technique when smelling the tubes. Never place the nose directly above a tube and inhale. The tube should be held a short distance from the nose and the odor wafted toward the nose by a fanning motion of the hand.

Lab Note: Destroy all bacteria with dilute household bleach before disposal down a sink.

Data and Observations

   a. Soup, open; cloudy; blue turns red; spoiled
   b. Soup, sealed; clear; no change; meaty or salty
   c. Water, open; clear; no change; none
   d. Water, sealed; clear; no change; none

Questions and Conclusions

1. only the open tube with soup; the sealed tube with soup and both water tubes
2. open soup tube; sealed tube with soup and both water tubes
3. the open soup tube
4. both soup tubes; both water tubes
5. The sealed soup tube had no bacteria.
6. Water does not supply food. No bacteria were found in the water tubes.
7. Boiling killed any bacteria that may have already been present in the soup or water.
8. All bacteria present in soup were not destroyed during boiling.
9. The only source of bacteria in this experiment was air, so we must inhale these organisms when we breathe.
10. Both tubes would remain clear. No bacteria would be present; Boiling destroys bacteria. Sealing prevents bacteria from entering the tubes.
11. Both tubes would become cloudy due to bacterial growth. Bacteria from the air would enter the soup and grow.
12. Both tubes would become cloudy due to bacterial growth.

Lab Note: Prepare extra open tubes of soup and place them in a refrigerator. Compare them each day with those left open at room temperature. Less cloudiness should result in the refrigerated tubes because cold temperatures slow the growth of bacteria. This is why many foods once opened must be refrigerated. Milk and other dairy products also are refrigerated for this reason. Freezing reduces bacterial growth even more.

Chapter 2   Traits and How They Change

Laboratory Activity 1 (page 7)

Data and Observations
Answers will vary.

Questions and Conclusions

1. Answers will vary but should reflect the decision to choose a trait that would create two different groups of beans.
2. Answers will vary. Making the sub-groups might be easier or more difficult depending on the traits chosen.
3. Most bags of mixed beans contain 10–15 different kinds of beans. Each bean is produced by a different kind of plant, with different growing requirements. Some bean plants might grow best in a certain type of environment, while other bean plants may grow best in another type. Also, different cultures prefer specific types of beans in the foods they eat.

Laboratory Activity 2 (page 9)

Data and Observations
Data will vary.

Questions and Conclusions
1. One; one-hundred million
2. Not all seeds are able to grow into new plants; some seeds are eaten by animals; too little or too much moisture might prevent some seeds from sprouting; abrupt changes in the weather might prevent some seeds from sprouting; wind might carry seeds to an unfavorable location; fire or extreme cold might prevent some seeds from sprouting.
3. Chances are very low that one-hundred-million green pepper plants will result from the seeds of one plant. Environmental factors, like those described in question 2, prevent this from happening.
4. Because many factors may prevent new organisms from growing, it makes sense for organisms to overproduce. By overproducing, the survival of the species is assured.
5. Natural selection and mutation can help the survival of a species.

Chapter 3   Interactions of Human Systems

Laboratory Activity 1 (page 13)

Lab note: You might want to have students bring in labels in advance to be sure you have multiple copies in each category.

Data and Observations

Table 1
Answers will vary, but students should include a variety of foods for each meal, and the correct mineral content data.
1. Answers will vary.
2. Answers will vary, but should correspond to the needs expressed in question 1.
3. **a.** cheddar cheese
   b. No; the minimum daily requirement is 1,000 mg. You would also need to eat other foods rich in calcium to keep your bones strong.

Questions and Conclusions
1.-4. Answers will vary according to the students' selections.
5. Students should answer "Yes", but explanations will vary. Different minerals help different aspects of a body's health and growth. A variety of foods is necessary to fill the varied mineral requirements of the human body.

Laboratory Activity 2 (page 19)

Data and Observations
Answers will vary, depending on the measurements and observations they make.

Questions and Conclusions
1. The chemical began to dissolve in the water. As the dissolved particles floated in the water, they began to rise and spread throughout the entire test tube, coloring the water purple.
2. Cells get some of their nutrients by having them diffuse across their membranes.
3. Yes; the water made the bag swell up, resembling a sausage.
4. No; the corn syrup appeared to stay inside the bag. No dark color was observed outside the bag.
5. The water molecules are small and can move across the bag. The sugar molecules are too big to leave the small holes in the bag.
6. Semipermeable means that only molecules of a certain size can pass across a membrane. Large molecules are kept in or out of a cell.

Chapter 4   Interactions of Life

Laboratory Activity 1 (page 23)

Data and Observations
Answers will vary, but should include some producers and some consumers.

Table 1
Sample answers:
Farm—people, hens, cows, corn, trees
Forest—trees, rabbits, birds, deer, squirrel
Desert—cactus, lizards, snake, jackrabbit
Ocean—seaweed, fish, clams, snails, funicates

Table 2
Student answers will vary depending on which type of community was studied. 1.–5. Answers will vary.

Questions and Conclusions
1. A community includes all the populations in an ecosystem.
2. an organism that makes its own food
3. an organism that can't make its own food, getting its energy-rich substance by eating producers or other consumers
4. Most communities have both. A community of producers can exist without consumers, but consumers can't survive without producers.
5. Answers will vary, but students should realize that all plants are producers.
6. Answers will vary, but students should realize that all animals are consumers.
7. Communities will have more producers than consumers. Producers, which supply food to the consumers, are at the bottom of the food chain.
8. food, in the form of energy-rich substances

Laboratory Activity 2 (page 27)

Data and Observations

Tables 1 and 3 and Figure 1
Answers will vary.

Questions and Conclusions
1. The fox is the predator. The rabbit is the prey.
2. Answers will vary. Students should be specific about the differences.

3. harsh winter, inadequate food, disease, decreased pheasant population
4. plentiful food, early spring
5. disease among the rabbits, inadequate food, hunting of foxes

6. availability of pheasants, larger litters, plentiful food
7. The foxes ate more rabbits, and the rabbit population declined.

Chapter 5   The Nonliving Environment

Laboratory Activity 1 (page 31)

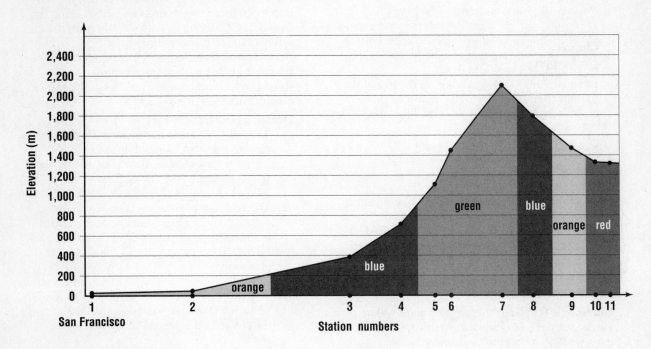

Questions and Conclusions
1. the western side because most of the water vapor carried by the wind condenses and falls as rain or snow before the air reaches the eastern side of the mountains
2. because Baxter is at a higher elevation than Auburn
3. Blue Canyon and Soda Springs because they are the highest elevations and more water vapor condenses and falls as precipitation
4. By the time the air from the Pacific Ocean reaches Reno, it has already lost much of its water vapor.
5. on the western side because environments that have plenty of water usually support large and more diverse population

Laboratory Activity 2 (page 35)
Lab Note: Plastic boxes must be identical in size and tall enough for the cups to fit inside when the lids are sealed. Plastic cups should be large enough to hold at least 150 mL of water.

Data and Observations
Lab Note: Data will vary, but should generally indicate the air temperature in Box B increased at a faster rate and reached a higher temperature than in Box A.

Graph
Graphs should accurately reflect students' data.

Questions and Conclusions
1. Bubbles of gas formed, rose to the top of the water, and entered the air.
2. The air temperature in Box B increased at a faster rate and reached a higher temperature than in Box A.
3. An increase in the amount of carbon dioxide in the atmosphere can cause air temperatures to increase.

Chapter 6   Ecosystems

Laboratory Activity 1 (page 39)

Questions and Conclusions
1. Pot 1 will show more growth than pot 2. The grass in pot 2 will probably be yellow and have very few leaves. Comparison to hypothesis will vary.
2. Pot 1 should grow the best. Pot 3 should show good growth but will probably be yellow from over-watering. Pot 4 will probably be wilted and not show healthy growth.
3. Grasses are tough and fast-growing and can usually grow in the wide open areas that are characteristic of primary succession.

4. A climax community usually has more trees and tall plants that would prevent light from reaching grasses and allowing them to thrive. Although grasses could still grow, their role in the community would not be the same as it is during succession. Thus, a climax community would have fewer grasses than a community still in succession.

Laboratory Activity 2 (page 41)

Questions and Conclusions

1. Answers may vary, but generally they will find organisms in all parts since ponds tend to be shallow and sunlight usually penetrates to the bottom.
2. Temperature and amount of light are among the factors that can vary with depth.
3. a. Answers may vary depending on the area of the country and the effect of the season on that area.
   b. Answers may vary, but absence of light could be a factor.
   c. Answers may vary, but if sunlight can't reach the bottom of the pond, this will affect the organisms found.
   d. Answers may vary, but the only clear water in a pond tends to be in its center. This could affect what is found as you move away from the shore.
4. Answers may vary, but some factors mentioned may be fertilizer runoff, sewage, acid precipitation, etc.

Chapter 7   Plate Tectonics

Laboratory Activity 1 (page 45)

Lab Note: It is unlikely that any two maps will be exactly the same. Map should be fairly split on the interpretation of location X as land or water.

Questions and Conclusions

1. Most students will indicate that it was land because it is located between places where fossils of small mammals and dinosaurs were found.
2. Answers will vary, because it is located between areas where fossils of land organisms and ocean organisms were found.
3. Because it is located between areas where fossils of land organisms and ocean organisms were found, some students will make it land while others will make it ocean. You could only know for sure if you found Mesozoic fossils at that location.
4. Answers will vary, depending on where students drew the shoreline of the land near location H.
5. The continent must have moved. During the Mesozoic it must have been located near the equator for corals to have grown in the oceans.

Laboratory Activity 2 (page 49)

Data and Observations

Students' data will vary. When observing the bubbles at the beginning of the experiments, students should notice that the bubbles tend to collect under the pieces of foam and coalesce. Bubbles will grow larger and larger until they slip to the sides of the foam and escape. Where two pieces of foam are touching, the bubbles will escape fairly vigorously. Eventually they will almost explode or pop. This action should lead students to consider the pressure and activity of magma and volcanoes at continental plate margins. When students observe the movement of their foam pieces during a full boil, they should see that the pieces are circulated from the center of the pot up to the top and out to the sides of the pot. There they will either get stuck or recirculate. Either way it is important that students draw inferences about the behavior and motion of crustal plates from the activity of their foam continents.

At the end of the experiment most students will not see much change in their foam continents. They should conclude that unlike real plates, the foam ones did not melt or break apart.

Questions and Conclusions

1. The bubbles were stuck under the foam. They grew together and formed one large bubble. Then the large bubbles floated to the sides of the foam where they burst up between two pieces of foam.
2. The action of the bubbles is similar to that of a volcano. The bubbles were like magma that increases in pressure at weak points along plate boundaries. It escapes like the bubbles in an explosion.
3. At first it seemed as though the foam went all over the place. After a while, the pattern was noticeable: the foam went down at the sides of the pot and up in the middle of the boiling water.
4. The tectonic plates move along the hot liquid mantle just like the foam. When they cannot move any farther they get stuck, like the Indian plate, or go under, like the Pacific plate.
5. This experiment is different because the foam never changed shape or cracked. In the real world, the plates change according to the kinds of forces acting on them. As a result, the plates of crust are moved by convection currents and broken up on the boiling surface of the mantle.
6. If the convection currents in the mantle changed direction or stopped, the tectonic plates would also stop. Everything would stay right where it is. Volcanoes and earthquakes might stop.

Chapter 8   Earthquakes and Volcanoes

Laboratory Activity 1 (page 53)

Data and Observations

Students' data will vary. Sample data is given below.
1. @ 2 cm, Faint circular waves appeared on the surface of the water. No water spilled out.
2. @ 8 cm, Circular waves appeared. They were easier to see than in the first trial. No water spilled out.

3. @ 14 cm, Larger circular waves appeared. A small trickle of water spilled down one side of the bowl.

4. @ 20 cm, Even larger waves appeared. This time, water spilled down two sides of the bowl. More water spilled out than in the previous trial.

Questions and Conclusions

1. Energy released by an earthquake travels outward from the focus in the form of seismic waves. Similarly, the waves that resulted from the book falling were produced by released energy. In this case, the energy came from a falling book rather than an actual earthquake. This released energy traveled outward in the form of waves through the table, into the bowl, and into the water, much like seismic waves travel through Earth and along its surface.

2. The amount of water spilling out of the bowl indicates the amplitude of the waves. Therefore, trials in which no water was spilled involved waves with smaller amplitudes than those in which water did spill.

3. Increasing the height from which the book was dropped increased the magnitude of the model earthquake. The higher the book, the more potential energy it had and the more energy it released when it fell. As the magnitude of the model earthquake increased, so did the amplitude of the waves produced in the detector.

4. You could set up two detectors on opposite ends of a table. Then you could drop a book closer to one of the detectors than the other. If more water spilled out of the detector closer to the book, you would know that the amplitude of the waves decreases with distance traveled. If more water spilled out of the detector farther from the book, you would know that the amplitude of the waves increases with distance traveled.

Laboratory Activity 2 (page 55)

Data and Observations

Students should observe that the plaster begins to crack as the balloons expand.

Students' data in Tables 1 and 2 will vary. However, they should find that the radius of the debris field in Part A increases with the size of the balloon. In Part B, they should find that the diameter and height of the "volcano" increase as more toothpaste is added. They should also find that the diameter of the flow is much larger than its height.

Questions and Conclusions

1. The large balloons modeled magma under the greatest pressure. The large balloons contain the most air. The more air a balloon contains, the more it stretches and the greater the pressure inside it.

2. As the size of the balloon increased, so did the distance the pieces of plaster were thrown. The size of the balloon indicates the amount of pressure inside

it, and the radius of the debris field indicates the force of the explosion. Therefore, the results show that as pressure in a volcano increases, so does the explosive force of an eruption.

3. The eruption modeled in Part A was explosive. Therefore, the volcano being modeled could be a cinder cone volcano or a composite volcano. Cinder cone volcanoes throw tephra into the air as they erupt explosively, and composite volcanoes sometimes erupt violently by releasing large amounts of ash and gas.

4. The inflation of the balloons modeled the expansion of gases inside heated magma. The cracks in the plaster indicated the force of the pressure that builds up inside the volcano.

5. a. In general, the second layer of toothpaste flowed over the top of the first layer, and the third layer flowed over the second.
   b. This result suggests that the top layer of basaltic lava was deposited more recently than the layers underneath it.

6. The layers of toothpaste were much wider than they were tall. Shield volcanoes have this broad, flat shape.

7. The types of "lava" produced by each model were very different. In Model A, the pieces of plaster represented tephra thrown into the air by an explosive eruption. The "tephra" was solid and irregularly shaped. In Model B, the toothpaste represented basaltic lava. It did not fly through the air, but flowed smoothly over the cardboard. In Model A, the eruption happened quite suddenly, while the eruption of Model B occurred more slowly. In both models, newer layers of lava or tephra built up on top of older layers. In addition, pressure played a role in both eruptions.

Chapter 9   Clues to Earth's Past

Laboratory Activity 1 (page 59)

Questions and Conclusions

1. Layer A; It is on the bottom and, by the principle of superposition, is the oldest.

2. The beds have been folded upward into an anticline.

3. The folding predated the glaciation and subsequent deposition of the glacial till.

4. The glacier withdrew and vegetation was able to grow. Then a second advance occured.

5. no; The topography is too smooth; If the area had been mountainous it would have had valley glaciers; hanging valleys, horns, and steep walled valleys would be left.

6. two

7. Beds A,B, and C were deposited and then uplifted and folded into an anticline. Erosion removed bed C and part of Bed B from the top of the anticline. The area then was covered by a continental glacier that deposited a layer of till as it withdrew. During

a period of warming and weathering, peat and soil were formed on the till. Another advance of the ice was followed by a retreat, and the second layer of till was deposited.

Laboratory Activity 2 (page 63)

Data and Observations
Students' sketches will vary with the objects they choose.

Questions and Conclusions
1. If a fossil appears in soils and rocks from many time periods, it does not isolate and identify when the organism existed.
2. Yes
3. Yes, both fossils are from the same type of organism
4. No, the soil in the bottom layer was laid down first. The fossils in the bottom layer are older than the fossils in the middle layer. A lived during both time periods.
5. what fossils are located in which layers of soil
6. Answers will vary Results should be similar. If the containers were disturbed during excavation, the fossils could have shifted. Results would be invalid
7. It is important to note that index fossils are found only during a specific time period. Fossils that are found nearby are close in age. If another like fossil is found from a different time, you can infer that the second plant or animal lived longer than the index fossil object. Whether the second fossil is found above or below or below the index fossil helps to determine time spans when that organism existed

Chapter 10   Geologic Time

Laboratory Activity 1 (page 67)

Data and Observations
1. eye color, height, hair color, skin color—Students may think of others.

Table 1
Answers will vary.

Table 2
Answers will vary.

Questions and Conclusions
1. Height, upright walking, ability to communicate with each other with verbal and written languages are possible answers.
2. Answers will vary.
3. Answers will vary, but height should be somewhat shorter.
4. The members of the species have become taller.
5. By watching how one characteristic changes over time, scientists can date fossils.
6. The changes take place over a much longer time span (millions of years) when dealing with fossils.

Laboratory Activity 2 (page 69)
Lab Note: You may need to remind students that 1,000 million years equals 1 billion years.

Data and Observations
Table 1
Precambrian Time; 3.456 billion years or 3 billion, 456 million years
Paleozoic Era; 299 million years
Mesozoic Era; 180 million years
Cenozoic Era; 65 million years
Graph
Should show data accurately, making clear the enormous difference in the length of the Precambrian Era as compared with of the each of the other three Eras.
Timeline
Specific representations will vary slightly, but should clearly show the relative differences among the Eras. Art should be relative and pertinent to the Era with which it is associated.

Questions and Conclusions
1. Precambrian time is the longest division; the Cenozoic Era is the shortest division.
2. about 2.1 times longer
3. in the Cenozoic Era; in the Holocene Epoch
4. at least 30 times longer; exact answers will vary depending on numbers used for calculations.
5. Answers will vary, but might include that the most recent events were difficult to mark and illustrate because the time periods represent such a small part of the time line.

Chapter 11   The Sun-Earth-Moon System

Laboratory Activity 1 (page73)

Data and Observations
Table 1—Answers will vary depending on the accuracy of the student.
Table 2—You may wish to have students show their velocity calculations.

Questions and Conclusions
1. the point on the equator
2. the point at 60° N
3. the point on the North Pole
4. the latitude or the distance north or south of the equator
5. The linear velocity decreases from the equator to the poles.

Laboratory Activity 2 (page 75)

Data and Observations
Students' drawings will vary but should demonstrate an understanding of the activity.

Questions and Conclusions
1. Students should note that only the tip of the cardboard is visible at first, then the complete triangle is visible.
2. As a ship approaches from across the ocean, the top of the ship comes into view first, followed by the remainder of the ship.
3. The tip of the cardboard comes into view first because the cardboard is moving over a curved

Teacher Guide & Answers (continued)

surface—the basketball. Similarly, the top of the ship at sea comes into view first because the ship is moving over a curved surface—Earth.

4. Students should note that the shadow cast by the textbook was rectangular while the shadow cast by the basketball was round.
5. If Earth were flat, its shadow would look like a flat "bar" on the moon during a lunar eclipse. Instead, Earth casts a curved shadow on the moon.
6. The basketball, a round object, casts a curved shadow. The textbook, a flat object, casts a sharp-edged shadow. Thus, Earth's curved shadow on the moon during a lunar eclipse is evidence of Earth's round shape.
7. Answers will vary. Students may mention photographs of Earth from space or their own observations of other objects in space, such as the Sun and moon. Accept all reasonable answers.

Chapter 12   The Solar System

Laboratory Activity 1 (page 77)

Table 1
Answers will vary, but data should show higher temperatures with the lid on.

Questions and Conclusions
1. The lid reflected the heat back into the box; no heat could escape into the air.
2. Some of the solar energy that reaches Earth's surface is trapped by carbon dioxide gas. This process heats the atmosphere near the surface.
3. The lid prevents the longwave radiation from escaping by absorbing some of the energy. On Earth some energy leaks back to space.
4. Sunlight striking Venus's surface is absorbed and reradiated as longwave radiation. The atmosphere, rich in CO_2, traps this radiation close to the planet's surface, thus heating it.
5. Carbon dioxide present in both atmospheres absorbs the reradiated energy from the surface. The atmosphere of Venus is more dense, however, and more heat is retained by the large amounts of carbon dioxide.

Laboratory Activity 2 (page 81)

Data and Observations
Students' observations will vary depending on how well they performed the experiment. Most should observe that the wind from the fan blew beads of melting water away from the fan. If the fan was strong enough it should have blown some sand particles along with the water. However, it is important that the students observe that the water was ejected farther from the fan than the sand because of the density. An astute student will recognize the pattern between a dwindling comet tail and the water pattern on the paper.

Questions and Conclusions
1. They were both blown away from the fan. The water moved the farthest.
2. Wind from the fan was powerful enough to eject water and sand particles from their original position. The particles were always thrown away from the wind source.
3. The solar wind comes from the Sun in every direction. As the comet nears the Sun, the hot solar wind melts the ice in the comet. The melted ice and dust it held are forced behind the comet, away from the Sun. This is why the tail of a comet always points away from the Sun.
4. The dust and water from a comet fly off into space where they float around as cosmic debris. Because it is so cold in space, the water freezes back into ice crystals.
5. Yes. It is possible that when its orbit is far from the Sun, the comet will attract dust and water crystals from space. However, this would not be enough to keep it from eventually dying out or crashing into a planet or moon.

Chapter 13   Stars and Galaxies

Laboratory Activity 1 (page 85)

Data and Observations
Students' data will vary depending on the relative brightnesses of the flashlights used.

Hypothesis for the Dispersal of Light
The closer the flashlight, the more intense, or brighter, the light because the rays of light do not disperse as far, hence the circle of light appears to grow smaller as the distance decreases.

Questions and Conclusions
1. The farther from the wall, the dimmer the light, because the light—shown from that point—is scattered widely, or diffused. Brightness, or intensity, decreases when distance is increased.
2. The light increased in brightness, or intensity, as distance decreased. When the light focuses, or concentrates, on a smaller space, it is not diffused, so it appears to shine more brightly.
3. The closer the star, the brighter it will appear, because its light will not be diffused, or scattered.
4. Repeating the experiment with a bigger and brighter flashlight would result in recording a greater intensity of light at the farthest distance. This is because the absolute magnitude of the brighter flashlight is greater. It will give off more light, so more light reaches the wall with greater intensity; hence, light shown from the same distance as the weaker flashlight will also have a greater apparent magnitude.
5. Position the student with the weak light close to the wall so that its apparent magnitude is strong—the circle of light is intense, or bright.

Science   171

Then position the student with the strong flashlight farther from the wall, until the two circles of light nearly match in intensity. At this point, one could say that they share the same apparent magnitude, even though the stronger flashlight, of course, has the greater absolute magnitude.

6. Position both students at the same distance and compare the circles of light each casts on the wall. The stronger flashlight, with the greater absolute magnitude, will also have the greater apparent magnitude.

7. Answers will vary. Students may mention comparing the star to others, using what they know about other objects in the night sky, or even using parallax. It is always good to study an object over a long period to detect changes and to learn more about it.

Laboratory Activity 2 (page 89)

Lab Note: Discuss the meanings of *spectrum* and *spectral analysis*. Introduce the cut-outs on page 15 of the lab with students and review how each cut-out will be used in the lab.

Data and Observations
Table 1
A—iron, calcium, sodium, hydrogen, helium
B—iron, sodium, hydrogen; the standard
C—iron, sodium, hydrogen; answers will vary.
D—iron, sodium, hydrogen, mercury; answers will vary.

Questions and Conclusions
1. Student answers will vary; Red, as there are a lot of lines in the red wavelengths.
2. B, C, and D. It should be noted that Star D has the same composition, but the spectral lines are slightly shifted to the red wavelengths.
3. Star D's spectral lines are shifted toward the red part of the spectrum. The star is moving away from the observer.
   Lab Note: You might review the Doppler effect with students.
4. Star C's spectral lines are wider than star B's.
   Lab Note: This could be caused by any one of the reasons given in the paragraph above.

Chapter 14   Inside the Atom

Laboratory Activity 1 (page 93)

Data and Observations
1. Student answers will vary based on their understanding of atoms. Students that already understand how small molecules are will predict that the vanilla molecules will seep out of the balloon and the area will smell strongly of vanilla.
2. The area smelled strongly of vanilla.

Questions and Conclusions
1. The vanilla molecules are small enough to move through the walls of the balloon.

2. The results indicate that the vanilla molecules are extremely small.
3. Helium atoms are so small that they pass through the walls of the balloon.
4. The helium atoms are smaller and will leak more quickly from the balloon than will the larger molecules in the vanilla.

Laboratory Activity 2 (page 95)

Data and Observations
Red: $4 \times 2 = 8$; $2 \times 1 = 2$; $(8 + 2)/(4 + 2) = 10/6 = 1.7$
Green: $3 \times 4 = 12$; $3 \times 3 = 9$; $(12 + 9)/(3 + 3) = 21/6 = 3.5$

Questions and Conclusions
1. Each color candy represented a different element, so the mass units were different. Also, the two groups had different numbers of each type of candy, even though the total number of candies was the same.
2. Y-12: $100 \times 12 = 1200$
   Y-14: $10 \times 14 = 140$
   Total: $(1200 + 140)/(100 + 10) = 1340/110 = 12.18$ units.
3. The atomic masses on the periodic table are weighted averages of the isotopes. In this experiment, the two groups of candy pieces modeled samples with two isotopes of one element.
4. U-238 is the most common isotope. The atomic mass shown on the periodic table is close to 238.
5. Mass number is the sum of the number of protons and neutrons in an atom of an element; it is different for different isotopes of the same element. Atomic mass is the average mass of all the isotopes of an element as it occurs in nature.
6. Protium: 1 proton, 0 neutrons; atomic mass = 1
   Deuterium: 1 proton, 1 neutron; atomic mass = 2
   Tritium: 1 proton, 2 neutrons; atomic mass = 3

Chapter 15   The Periodic Table

Laboratory Activity 1 (page 97)

Questions and Conclusions
1. The graph peaks, falls into valleys, and rises again with a little peak appearing just before each of the high peaks.
2. alkali metals
3. halogens
4. noble gases
5. The radii increase. Each peak represents the beginning of a new period.
6. The radii become smaller. Each group of elements represents a period.
7. A graph of discovered elements predicts the atomic radii of any undiscovered elements that have atomic numbers within the range of the discovered elements. Undiscovered elements would be expected to have properties similar to discovered elements that occupy comparable positions on the graph.

8. Metals have larger radii than the nonmetals in the same period.

Laboratory Activity 2 (page 99)

Questions and Conclusions

1. 13 and 14; they are consecutive days that fit between 12 and 15.
2. Thursday
3. 11–17
4. Monday
5. period 1
6. the 31st and the second Saturday of next month, the 14th
7. Sunday
8. It occurs once per year at the same time.

Chapter 16   Atomic Structure and Chemical Bonds

Laboratory Activity 1 (page 101)

Lab Note: To prepare each 0.1 M solution, dissolve each in distilled water and dilute each to 1 liter:

   34.2 g sucrose
   18.0 g glucose
   5.9 g NaCl
   4.0 g NaOH
   5.6 mL H_2SO_4

(Caution: heat involved. Add slowly to 500 mL distilled water, then dilute to 1 liter.)

Lab Note: The NaOH and H_2SO_4 solutions are very dilute. As long as the teacher prepares the solutions, safety is not a concern. Also, there should not be any vapors.

Lab Note: Testing rock salt can illustrate the difference between conductivity in solution and as a solid. Sugar can be used for contrast.

Questions and Conclusions

1. The conductivity of distilled water is zero.
2. The conductivity of the distilled water was measured as a control. Because the conductivity of water is zero, any conductivity by a solution would indicate that the dissolved substances in the solution caused the conductivity.
3. Students should have observed conductivity in the 0.1M NaCl, 0.1M NaOH, and the 0.1M H_2SO_4 solutions. These solutions contained ions. The 0.1M glucose and 0.1M sucrose solutions contained no ions and should not have shown any conductivity.
4. The solutions of NaOH, H_2SO_4, sucrose, and glucose were made from covalent compounds. The H_2SO_4 and NaOH solutions did conduct an electric current.
5. Students should have observed no conductivity with either substance.
6. NaCl shows no conductivity in crystalline form, but is a good conductor in solution.
7. The results from this experiment indicate that ions in solution can conduct an electric current.

Laboratory Activity 2 (page 105)

Questions and Conclusions

Lab Note: To prepare each 0.1M solution, dissolve each in distilled water and dilute to 1 liter:

   37.5g Al $(NO_3)_3$ • $9H_2O$
   23.3g Cu$(NO_3)_2$ • 2 1/2 H_2O
   40.4g Fe$(NO_3)_3$ • $9H_2O$
   25.6g Mg $(NO_3)_2$ • $6H_2O$
   29.1g Ni$(NO_3)_2$ • $6H_2O$
   29.8g Zn$(NO_3)_2$ • $6H_2O$

Lab Note: 10-mm lengths of wire of each of the metals may be used

Data and Observations

1. 5
2. 0
3. 3
4. 6
5. 2
6. 4

Questions and Conclusions

1. These wells are controls with which to compare the color of the solutions in the wells to which metals had been added.
2. These wells are controls with which to compare the color of the metal strips in the wells to which solutions had been added.
3. The metal strips were cleaned to remove any dirt or materials that may have prevented a chemical reaction from taking place.
4. Mg, Al, Zn, Fe, Ni, Cu
5. Ions of Cu, Ni, Fe, Zn, Al, Mg—from the most active to the least
6. The more active the metal, the less active the ion, and vice versa.

Chapter 17   Chemical Reactions

Laboratory Activity 1 (page 109)

Lab Notes: to prepare a 0.1M solution, dissolve 25.0 g $CuSO_4$ • $5H_2O$ in distilled water, add 3 drops of 18M H_2SO_4, and dilute to 1 liter.

Data and Observations

1. silver-gray
2. Answers will vary.
3. dark gray-black
4. Answers will vary.
5. white solids and clear, colorless liquid
6. The flaming splint was extinguished.
7. Answers will vary.

Table 1

8. silver
9. dark blue
10. red
11. light blue

Questions and Conclusions

1. Iron in the steel wool and oxygen from the air are both reactants.

2. Heat raises the temperature and speeds up the reaction.
3. The bubbles are evidence of a gaseous product. The solids remaining in the test tube have changed appearance indicating a new solid was formed.
4. Energy in the form of heat had to be added before the $NaHCO_3$ changed into new products. The addition of energy suggests an endothermic reaction.
5. A color change on the surface of the iron nail and a lightening of the bluish color of the copper (II) sulfate suggest that at least two products were formed.
6. This reaction took place without adding heat, making it an exothermic reaction.

Laboratory Activity 2 (page 113)

Lab Note: Measure $1M$ of both the cobalt nitrate and the sodium hypochlorite solutions.

Data and Observations
1. Answers will vary.
2. Answers will vary.

Table 1
Student's data will vary.

Figure 4
Data will vary. In general, the slope of the line will increase as temperature increases.

Questions and Conclusions
1. Answers will vary. Students should notice that the slope, or steepness, of the graph increases as the temperature is raised.
2. Answers will vary. Students should conclude that increasing the temperature increases the reaction rate.
3. When the pipette bulb is squeezed to expel air in step 10, any solution in the stem would splatter and be lost.
4. The bottle at room temperature will go flat faster. The decomposition reaction goes at a faster rate at higher temperatures.

Chapter 18   Motion and Momentum

Laboratory Activity 1 (page 117)

Questions and Conclusions
1. Answers will vary, but should demonstrate an understanding that constant force results in a constant acceleration.
2. speed increases
3. The rate of acceleration remained constant.
4. Acceleration decreases as mass increases.
5. As the force increases, acceleration increases.
6. No movement would indicate that the skater's inertia was too great, and a force greater than 4-N would be required to move the skater.

Laboratory Activity 2 (page 121)

Questions and Conclusions
1. The faster trial is steeper and the slower trial is flatter.
2. It measures the speed of the object. The larger the slope, the faster an object travels. The smaller the slope, the slower the object.
3. It means the object has stopped.
4. A bowling ball dropped from a great height would fall at a constant rate of 9.8 m/s^2. The bowling ball in this lab negatively accelerated as it traveled.
5. Student answers will vary.
6. Student answers will vary.
7. Distance is how far an object moves. Displacement is the distance and direction of the object from the starting point.

Chapter 19   Force and Newton's Laws

Laboratory Activity 1 (page 125)

Questions and Conclusions
1. More weight on the block caused there to be more friction.
2. A change in surface area had no effect on the friction.
3. As the weight of the block increased, both the static-friction force and the sliding-friction force increased.
4. Static friction is always greater than sliding friction.
5. Answers may vary. One major source of error could be the fact that getting exact readings from the spring scale was difficult. Some guessing was involved.
6. The coefficients remained constant.
7. The coefficients remained constant.
8. No. The coefficient of sliding friction does not depend on the weight of the block. As the weight increases, the friction force increases in direct proportion. The ratio of the friction force to weight does not change.
9. No. The narrow and wide parts of the block produced identical results.
10. Explain. A high coefficient of friction would be best. High coefficients result in high friction forces for specific weights. High friction in tires allows them to hold onto the road well.

Laboratory Activity 2 (page 129)

Lab Note: It is important that the weight of the clay ball be enough to move the car but not so great that the car accelerates too fast for accurate timing. You may need to adjust the mass of the clay ball depending on the mass of the cars you use.

Questions and Conclusions
1. See students' graphs.

2. Newton's second law states that $F = m \times a$. The force (weight of the clay ball) is the same each time. Given the same force, a more massive object will accelerate more slowly. This slower acceleration was observed as mass was added to the car.
3. Even though the mass is the same, travel times can be slightly different. By averaging three travel times, you can be more certain that your number is close to the actual time.
4. Student responses will vary. Possible sources of error are reaction time in releasing the car and starting the stopwatch, reaction time in stopping the stopwatch when the car reaches the edge, faulty release of the car by either pushing it with fingers or having it stick, and friction between the table and the string.
5. Student responses will vary. To make the prediction, students should extend the graph line until it intersects the line for 15 s. Students should be able to explain how they arrived at their predictions.

Chapter 20   Work and Simple Machines

Laboratory Activity 1 (page 133)

Questions and Conclusions
1. The work was the same.
2. They should be the same because the values of the force acting on the 1-kg mass and the distance the mass moved each time were the same.
3. Answers will vary. Students should recognize that the student who raised the 1-kg mass in the shorter period of time developed more power.
4. Answers will vary. Students should recognize that each student lifted the mass at a different rate. Therefore, the time to lift the mass will differ for each student.
5. The amount of work is independent of the speed at which the 1-kg mass is lifted. The amount of power is directly related to the speed because the speed is related to the time needed to do the work.

Laboratory Activity 2 (page 137)

Lab Note: Be sure that every student does not bring in his or her bicycle. However, make sure there is a variety to be used by the class.

Data and Observations
1. If the pedals are rotated at a constant speed, the wheel speed should increase as the gears are shifted from low to high.
2. Answers will vary.

Table 1
Answers will vary.

Questions and Conclusions
1. A high mechanical advantage allows the riders to climb hills easily.
2. A greater speed advantage allows riders to travel farther and faster with a minimal number of pedal revolutions.

3. The wheels and gears involve wheels and axles. The gears also use pulleys. The gearshifts and the pedals are levers.
4. Inversely proportional; as mechanical advantage increases, speed advantage decreases.
5. The combination with the fewest number of teeth in front and the most number of teeth in back produced the greatest MA.
6. The combination with the most number of teeth in front and the fewest number of teeth in back produced the greatest SA.
7. When going up a large hill or riding across a slick surface, the friction between the ground and the tires is essential for balance and continued forward motion. When going around a corner, friction keeps the wheels from sliding out from under the bicycle.
8. Friction on the chain, the wheels and axles, and the gears reduces the efficiency of the bicycle.

Chapter 21   Thermal Energy

Laboratory Activity 1 (page 141)
Lab Note: Students can begin to set up for Part B while waiting for the ice to melt and water to heat for Part A. Make sure water for Part A does not reach boiling, however.

Data and Observations
Table 1
1. In the room-temperature water, the dye dropped fairly quickly to the bottom of the beaker. It then spread across the bottom. In about five minutes, the dye had diffused throughout the water.
2. In the beaker of cold water, the dye dropped to the bottom of the beaker sort of quickly but did not spread across the bottom very quickly. It was easy to see the dye drop for several minutes before it started to spread (diffuse) through the water. The dye moved more slowly than it did in the other two containers.
3. In the hot water, the dye moved really fast throughout the water. The water was colored almost instantaneously.

Table 2
Students data for the circumference measurements will vary. However, their observations on the differences in the circumference should show that the room temperature balloon shows no change or perhaps a slight decrease, the cold balloon shows a decrease, and the hot balloon shows an increase.

Questions and Conclusions
1. The circumference decreased. The heat from the air inside the balloon transferred into the colder outside air in the ice chest. When the temperature of the air inside decreased, the air molecules moved more slowly. They did not push out the edges of the balloon as far.

2. The hot balloon expanded. The air molecules had greater kinetic energy. They moved against the edge of the balloon with greater force and increased its circumference.
3. The room temperature balloon got a bit smaller because the air from the lungs is warmer than room temperature and has more thermal energy. As it cooled down to room temperature, the balloon got smaller.
4. The energy of the individual air molecules or atoms increased or decreased with the change in temperature. As the molecules gained or lost energy, their force against the rubber of the balloon increased or decreased and the size of the balloon changed accordingly.
5. in the beaker of water with the highest temperature
6. The fact that the dye was transported by the water molecules more quickly showed that the molecules were moving faster in the heated water. The dye spread throughout the beaker of heated water much faster than in the other beakers. The dye spread most slowly in the beaker with the coldest water.

Laboratory Activity 2 (page 145)

Data and Observations

Table 1
Students' data will vary, but the temperature of the dark container should be higher than that for the light container.

Figure 2
Students' graphs will vary with their experimental data. The two lines should be easily distinguished from each other. The line for the dark container should be above the line for the light container.
1. Answers will vary, but the temperature should be higher than in the light container.
2. Answers will vary, but the temperature should be lower than in the dark container.
3. Answers will vary, based on the temperature of the environment and sunlight availability. The amount of increase should be greater than that of the water in the light container.
4. Answers will vary, as in no. 3. The amount of increase should be less than that in the dark container.

Questions and Conclusions
1. Yes; The water in the dark container heated up more quickly.
2. Dark colors are better able to absorb solar radiation.
3. No; without sunlight, the dark container would not be able to absorb the solar radiation. Temperatures would stay about the same.
4. Answers will vary, but most students would rather wear a light-colored T-shirt in the desert because the light-colored shirt would not absorb the Sun's radiation as quickly as would a dark T-shirt.

Chapter 22   Electricity

Laboratory Activity 1 (page 149)

Data and Observations

Table 1
1. Predictions will vary; bulbs light; bulbs light
2. Predictions will vary; bulbs light; bulbs light
3. Predictions will vary; bulbs light; bulbs light
4. Predictions will vary; no change; no change
5. Predictions will vary; bulbs light; bulbs light
6. Predictions will vary; bulbs light; bulbs light
7. Predictions will vary; bulbs light; bulbs light
8. Predictions will vary; no change; no change
9. Predictions will vary; no change; no change
10. Predictions will vary; no change; no change
11. bulbs light on either initial or reversed connection

Questions and Conclusions
1. The list should include aluminum foil, brass screw, copper pipe, graphite, nail, paper clip, and sometimes a diode.
2. The list should include glass rod, plastic pen cap, rubber eraser, wooden stick, and sometimes a diode.
3. The diode appeared in both lists.
4. The bulbs light due to current in the circuit.
5. Students should have observed that all metal materials conducted well.
6. Graphite is a nonmetal.
7. Plastics, glass, wood, and rubber make good insulators.
8. A diode could be used to ensure that a current runs in one direction only.

Laboratory Activity 2 (page 153)

Data and Observations

Table 1
1. no changes; 0 volts
2. some bubbling; Answers will vary.
3. some bubbling; Answers will vary.
4. no changes; 0 volts

Questions and Conclusions
1. The battery conditions with the copper strip, aluminum foil, and hydrochloric acid should produce the highest voltage.
2. HCl produced the higher voltage because it is a stronger acid.
3. Bubbles were observed, and a voltage was produced.
4. Copper and aluminum together produced the best batteries
5. Students should observe little change in the appearance of the copper strip, but the aluminum foil should show definite evidence of corrosion.

Chapter 23   Magnetism

Laboratory Activity 1 (page 157)

Questions and Conclusions

1. north
2. The largest changes may have occured near metallic objects or wall outlets where appliances are drawing current.
3. Answers will vary. Electric current flowing in wires may have caused deflection to occur.
4.

The magnetic axis is about 11° away from the geographic axis. The magnetic declination will vary between 20° E to 20° W across the United States.

Laboratory Activity 2 (page 159)

Lab Note: Small disk magnets are readily available at craft and hobby stores. They are sold in packs for people who want to make refrigerator magnets.

Questions and Conclusions

1. Student responses will vary. Some codes will be read accurately, some will have the 1s and 0s reversed (B 1000→T 0111). If two groups labeled the same pole of the reader magnet "1," they will read the same code. If not, they will read the reverse.
2. Students could cooperate at the beginning of class to calibrate their magnets. Or they could add a calibration magnet to the beginning of the strip. It should represent 0 (or 1). If the reader magnet gives the wrong reading, they know to reverse each reading. (So 1001 becomes 0110.) If the reader magnet gives the right reading, use it normally.

Chapter 24   Waves, Sound, and Light

Laboratory Activity 1 (page 161)

Lab Note: Students may have to make several attempts before they get quality waves that they can evaluate.

Data and Observations

Step 2: The wave should be reflected back. The amplitude of the reflected wave will be less than the original wave.

Step 3: The waves will have constructive interference. The amplitudes of the original waves will add together to make a larger wave.

Step 4: The waves will have destructive interference. The amplitude of the final wave will be very small or zero.

Questions and Conclusions

1. The wave was reflected back but with less amplitude and less energy.
2. No, some of the energy was lost. The person holding the rope absorbed some of the energy.
3. The crests combined to make a larger wave. The crest and trough made a much smaller wave or canceled each other out.
4. When the waves met, the amplitudes were added together into a single wave. When two crests meet, the resultant wave is a larger wave. When a trough and crest from different waves meet, the resultant wave is a much smaller wave or no wave at all.
5. Add the amplitudes together like you would add a positive and negative number. A crest would have positive amplitude and a trough would have negative amplitude. The resultant wave would be the sum of the two amplitudes.

Laboratory Activity 2 (page 163)

Data and Observations

When the beaker contains only water, the beam of light is clearly visible on the index card. The light becomes fainter as more milk is added to the water. Finally the light will not be visible at all on the index card when enough milk as been added to the water.

Questions and Conclusions

1. The flashlight beam was clearly visible on the index card opposite the flashlight.
2. The flashlight beam became dimmer as more milk was added to the water.
3. The particles of milk fat scattered the light waves in the flashlight beam so that they traveled in many directions. As a result, the amount of light in the beam was reduced as the beam traveled through the beaker.